Common Core
Writing Companion

GRADE 7

D1296669

Perfection Learning®

EDITORIAL DIRECTOR:	CAROL FRANCIS
EXECUTIVE EDITOR:	JIM STRICKLER
EDITOR:	ANDREA STARK
PROOFREADING COORDINATOR:	SHERI COOPER
ART DIRECTION:	RANDY MESSER
DESIGNER:	TOBI CUNNINGHAM, EMILY ADICKES
COVER:	MIKE ASPENGREN

REVIEWERS: AMANDA PORTNER
Literacy Specialist
Thurmont Middle School
Thurmont, Maryland

CONNIE SMITHSON
English Teacher
Umatilla High School
Umatilla, Florida

PHOTO CREDITS: istockphoto.com: pp. 4, 35; dreamstime.com p. 14; photos.com: pp. 18, 24, 39, 44, 51, 59, 61, 63, 69, 74

© 2013 Perfection Learning®

www.perfectionlearning.com

All rights reserved. No part of this book may be reproduced, stored in a retrieval system, or transmitted in any form or by any means, electronic, mechanical, photocopying, recording, or otherwise, without the prior permission of the publisher. For information regarding permissions, write to: Permissions Department, Perfection Learning, 2680 Berkshire Parkway, Des Moines, Iowa 50325.

4 5 6   PP   18 17 16 15 14 13

91595
ISBN: 978-0-7891-8465-8

Printed in the United States of America

Table of Contents

Table of Contents *continued*

©Perfection Learning® • No Reproduction Permitted.

Meeting the Common Core State Standards

The Common Core State Standards declare the importance of writing to texts—of drawing knowledge from sources and using what you learn to help you express your ideas clearly:

> For students, writing is a key means of asserting and defending claims, showing what they know about a subject, and conveying what they have experienced, imagined, thought, and felt.

The instruction and activities in this book will prepare you to meet the standards. If you do, you will score well on the assessments based on them.

What Are the Characteristics of Good Writing?

Your writing will be evaluated according to how well it shows the basic characteristics found in all types of good writing:

- *Development:* Does the text state the key idea clearly and support it strongly?
- *Organization:* Does the text include an introduction, body, and conclusion? Are transitions from one idea to another smooth and logical?
- *Evidence:* Is the information in the text relevant and strong?
- *Language and Style:* Does the text use words precisely? Is the tone appropriate?
- *Grammar, Spelling, and Punctuation:* Does the text use standard grammar, spelling, and punctuation?

How Is This Book Organized?

The first chapter of this book provides instruction and activities to help develop the characteristics of good writing listed above.

Each of the next five chapters focuses on a different type of writing:

- arguments
- informative/explanatory texts
- research reports
- literary analyses
- narratives

In each of these five chapters, the first several lessons highlight the elements particularly important to one type of writing. For example, the chapter on arguments includes a lesson that focuses on claims.

The next to last lesson in each chapter takes you step-by-step through writing a text. Built into these lessons are instruction and practice in grammar and usage that address the most common writing problems.

The final lesson in each chapter provides prompts for you to demonstrate your skills in gathering, analyzing, and using information in your writing. This lesson ends with a checklist based on the characteristics of good writing.

Chapter 1

Characteristics of Good Writing

All writing shares common characteristics. These are important for you to understand and master to be an effective writer. Good writing

- is well-developed
- has a cohesive organization
- contains evidence from sources to support main points
- uses precise language and, in most cases, a formal style
- follows rules of standard grammar, spelling, and punctuation

LESSON 1 DEVELOPMENT

Well-developed writing focuses on one main idea. The writer expresses one central idea and then expands and supports it with interesting details, relevant facts, or carefully chosen evidence. Everything in the text should be appropriate to the task and the audience.

Writing for an Audience

When you write, think about your readers.

- Are the people who read your essay old or young?
- How much do your readers already know about your topic?
- What do your readers want to know from you?

 ### Activity 1A Finding the Main Idea

The following excerpt is from the Gettysburg Address, the speech delivered by Abraham Lincoln at the dedication of a military cemetery in 1863. Read the passage and answer the questions that follow.

We have come to dedicate a portion of it [a battlefield of the Civil War], as a final resting place for those who died here, that the nation might live. This we may in all propriety do. But, in a larger sense, we can not dedicate, we can not consecrate [make special], we can not hallow [make holy] this ground. The brave men, living and dead, who struggled here, have consecrated it, far above our poor power to add or detract. The world will little note, nor long remember what we say here, but it can never forget what they did here.

1. Summarize the central idea of this excerpt.

_____

2. Summarize the sentences that support the central idea.

_____

_____

_____

©Perfection Learning® • No Reproduction Permitted.

Activity 1B Writing a Paragraph

Read the following facts about President John Kennedy. Then complete the exercises below.

- Kennedy was born in 1917 in Brookline, Massachusetts.
- Kennedy was elected president in 1960.
- Kennedy was assassinated in Dallas, Texas, on November 22, 1963.
- Kennedy was the youngest person ever elected president.
- The most famous line of Kennedy's first speech as president was, "Ask not what your country can do for you—ask what you can do for your country."
- The closing line of Kennedy's first speech as president was, ". . . here on Earth, God's work must truly be our own."
- Kennedy's first speech as president was short, only 14 minutes long.

1. Write a checkmark before three statements you would use in a paragraph about John Kennedy for an audience of third-grade students.

2. State the central idea of your paragraph.

_____

_____

3. Write a paragraph for third-grade students. Include both your main idea and supporting details. Write the information in your own words. Do not copy the sentences from the list of facts.

_____

_____

_____

_____

_____

_____

_____

> **Technology and Level of Formality**
>
> You should adjust your writing according to your audience. On a social media site where you are writing just for your friends, you might choose to be very informal. However, if you are posting your comments on a blog about current events, you might choose to be more formal.

LESSON 2 ORGANIZATION

A well-organized text has a beginning, middle, and ending. It presents details in a logical order so that readers can follow the ideas easily. Transitional words and phrases express the connection between one idea and another. Using transitional words and phrases effectively will help your writing demonstrate unity and clarity.

Organizational Structure	Common Uses	Transitions
Chronological: by time order	• Narrative writing to explain events • Informational writing to explain steps in a process	• began • next • later • at the same time
Order of Importance: from least to most important or from most to least important	• Argumentative writing to explain reasons • Informational writing to explain details	• first • another reason • however • on the other hand
Spatial Order: by location	• Informational writing to describe places and things	• across • beneath • in the upper corner
Comparison and Contrast: according to similarities and differences	• Informational writing to show how things are alike or different	• similarly • in the same way • conversely

Activity 2A Analyzing an Excerpt

The following passage was written by Zitkala-Sa, a Dakota Sioux woman who is also known as Gertrude Bonnin. She recalls how as a young girl she tried to catch up with her own shadow. Read the passage and answer the questions that follow it.

> Standing straight and still, I began to glide after it, putting out one foot cautiously. When, with the greatest care, I set my foot in advance of myself, my shadow crept onward too. Then again I tried it; this time with the other foot. Still again my shadow escaped me. I began to run; and away flew my shadow, always just a step beyond me. Faster and faster I ran, setting my teeth and clenching my fists, determined to overtake my own fleet shadow. But ever swifter it glided before me, while I was growing breathless and hot.

   ©Perfection Learning® • No Reproduction Permitted.

1. List at least four transition words that connect ideas.

_____

_____

2. Of the four types of organization listed in the chart on the previous page, which one best describes the organization of the entire excerpt?

_____

Activity 2B Writing a Paragraph

Imagine you are writing a speech for a president who is running for reelection. Write a paragraph that includes at least three facts from the list below and at least three transition words or phrases.

- More adults are working than ever before.
- Air pollution is lower than it has been in fifty years.
- Immigrants flock to the United States in search of opportunity.
- About twenty-two percent of children live in poverty.
- Homicides are the second leading cause of death among teenagers.
- Many schools reduced their staffs last year because they lacked money.

_____

_____

_____

_____

_____

_____

_____

_____

_____

Essay Organization

The beginning of a text is the **introduction.** In most essays and research reports, it is just one paragraph.

The middle part of a text is the **body.** It is the longest of the three parts of a text. It includes almost all of the information you want your reader to know.

The ending of a text is the **conclusion.** In most essays and research reports, it is just one paragraph.

Collaboration on Organization

Discuss with a classmate how to organize the information in your paragraph. Consider in which order you want to present the facts.

LESSON 3 EVIDENCE

Often a prompt will ask you to develop your essay by providing evidence. To gather evidence, read texts closely, paying attention to each detail. The specific information that you find in a reading, such as quotations, statistics, informed judgments, and logical reasons, is called **textual evidence**.

Annotating Text

Interacting with what you read helps you understand it, remember it, and use it for evidence in your writing. When reading printed materials you own, **annotate,** or write on, the pages. For example:

- Underline key ideas and definitions.
- Circle unfamiliar terms.
- Draw arrows to connect related ideas.
- Number steps in a process or events in a story.
- Write questions about ideas you don't understand.
- Write summaries of key ideas.

In addition, use stars, boxes, and other marks to help you highlight other features of the text. For example, if you are focusing on the author's use of colors as symbols, put a star in the margin beside each mention of a color. See page 49 for an example of annotation.

If you do not own the material you are reading, write your annotations on sticky notes or on another sheet of paper. If you are reading an electronic text, find out what options you have for annotating the file.

> **Conversation with the Writer**
>
> One way to think about annotating text is to imagine the writer is sitting across the table from you as you read.
>
> - What questions would you ask the writer?
> - What feedback would you give the writer?
>
> Include your questions and feedback as annotations.

Activity 3A Identifying Textual Evidence

Cool Papa Bell was one of the greatest baseball players of all time. He played from 1922 to 1950, during a time when professional baseball was divided into separate leagues for white and black players. Bell played in what were called the Negro Leagues. Underline three examples of textual evidence you could use in an essay about Bell for a local newspaper story about outstanding but little-known baseball players.

> [Cool Papa Bell] was the fastest man in all of baseball. He was like lightning. Cool Papa could circle the bases in twelve to thirteen seconds. One minute he was standing still on first base, and next thing you know, he was slowing up at third. More than once he scored from first base on a bunt. He was so fast, Jesse Owens, the Olympic sprinter, wouldn't race him without his track shoes.
>
> Source: Nelson, Kadir. *We Are the Ship: The Story of Negro League Baseball.* New York: Hyperion, 2008. Page 42. Print.

 ©Perfection Learning® • No Reproduction Permitted.

LESSON 4 LANGUAGE AND STYLE

Effective writing is precise and clear. Precise language includes words that help readers "see" what is being described. It uses nouns and verbs that are specific rather than general. **Style** is a writer's individual way of expressing ideas. In general, for classroom assignments and on tests, you should use a formal style. When writing formally, you should avoid slang words and personal pronouns.

Activity 4A Analyzing a Paragraph

Read the following paragraph from "The Snake," a short story by John Steinbeck. Underline three examples of precise language.

> Dr. Phillips climbed the wooden steps and opened the door. The white rats in their cages scampered up and down the wire, and the captive cats in their pens mewed for milk. Dr. Phillips turned on the glaring light over the dissection table and dumped his clammy sack on the floor.

Activity 4B Writing a Paragraph

Choose one of your favorite topics in math or science. Write a paragraph, using precise language and formal style, that explains why you like this topic.

_____

_____

_____

_____

_____

_____

_____

_____

©Perfection Learning® • No Reproduction Permitted.

The Power of Precise Language

What is the difference between these two sentences?

- He said "Stop!" as he went after the car.

- He screamed "Stop!" as he sprinted after the car.

Notice how making a few words more precise makes the second sentence much clearer—and much more engaging.

Collaboration on Evaluation

Evaluate a partner's paragraph for these traits:

- Identify at least three examples of precise language.

- Identify any slang, personal pronouns, or other language that seems informal.

LESSON 5 CONVENTIONS IN WRITING

To make your writing easy for your audience to follow, you should use words and symbols as your readers expect you to. That is, you should use the proper conventions in the following areas:

- **grammar,** which is the study of how words are related to each other in a sentence

- **spelling,** which is the sequence of letters that form a word

- **punctuation,** which is the use of marks such as periods and commas to make the meanings of words clear

Activity 5A Editing a Paragraph

Edit the paragraph for mistakes in grammar, spelling, and punctuation by rewriting it correctly on the lines below.

> The singer nown as Selena born in Lake Jackson Texas, in 1971. she performed in both Spanish and English, she would succede in wining fans throughout latin america and the United States Most critics would conceed that she was one of the top bilingual singers ever. she was selected for the Latin Music Hall of Fame in 1995. In 2011, the United States Post Office features her on a stamp.

Spelling the "Seed" Sound

Words that end with the "seed" sound are usually spelled *–cede*. Examples: precede, concede, recede.

- A few words end in *–ceed:* exceed, proceed, succeed.

- One common English word ends in *–sede:* supersede.

Collaborating on Editing

Use the following to evaluate a partner's edited paragraph for Activity 5A:

- Are the spelling errors corrected?

- Are the verb tenses correct throughout the paragraph?

- Do the subjects and verbs agree in number?

- Are commas used correctly?

©Perfection Learning® • No Reproduction Permitted.

Writing an Argumentative Essay

How do you get someone to agree with you? One way is to write your ideas in a way that gets them to see an issue the same way you do. This is called writing an **argumentative essay.**

LESSON 1 CLAIMS

In the first paragraph of an argumentative essay, you should make a claim. A **claim** is the main point you want your readers to agree with. A good claim should be a precise statement that you think is true, but that some people disagree with. It is a statement that people can use reasons and evidence to support. Are these statements good claims?

- "Wrestling and basketball are both sports." This is not a good claim because it is a statement that no one would disagree with.

- "I like wrestling more than I like basketball." This is not a good claim because it is a personal opinion that no one could argue with. It depends only on what you prefer.

- "Wrestling requires a broader range of skills than basketball so it is a better sport for students to learn." This is a well-written claim. It is precise and a judgment, and one not everyone will agree with. People could support or oppose it using reasons and evidence.

- "All students should take a one-semester financial literacy course in middle school so they are prepared to use money wisely." This is a well-written claim. It is a precise, debatable judgment.

> ### Defining Words
>
> Many claims are about how to define a word precisely. For example, most people agree that bullying is bad. However, people disagree over what they mean by *bullying*.

Activity 1A Analyzing Claims

Note why each statement is a weak claim.

Statement	Weakness
1. The Mexican grizzly bear went extinct in the 1960s.	
2. I wish I could have seen a Mexican grizzly bear.	
3. A Russian, Yuri Gagarin, was the first human to travel in outer space.	
4. I think Yuri Gagarin was very brave.	

Activity 1B Writing Claims

Write two claims that would fit at the end of the following paragraph.
One should argue in favor of keeping art and music classes. The other
should argue in favor of focusing more on reading, writing, and math.

> The three r's, "reading, 'riting, and 'rithmetic," have been the
> core of education in the United States since the 1800s. In recent
> years, parents and teachers have been concerned about how well
> students are learning these basic skills. Out of this concern, many
> schools have dropped art and music classes so that students can
> spend more time learning to read, to write, and to do math.

Counterclaims

Statements that disagree with your claim are called **counterclaims.** In an argumentative essay, you should present and respond to counterclaims.

Claim in favor of keeping art and music classes	Claim in favor of focusing more on reading, writing, and math
1.	2.

©Perfection Learning® • No Reproduction Permitted.

LESSON 2 SUPPORT FOR CLAIMS

To win your readers to your point of view, you need to support your claim as strongly as you can. Most support is one of two kinds, either evidence or reasons. **Evidence** includes facts, such as definitions, statistics, and informed judgments.

- A **definition** states the meaning of a word. Example: The pulmonary artery is the vessel that carries blood from the heart to the lungs.

- A **statistic** is a number that describes information. Example: The human body includes about 60 miles of blood vessels

- An **informed judgment** is the opinion of people with knowledge about a topic that they can support. Example: According to the world-famous Mayo Clinic, eating lots of fatty foods contributes to the condition people call hardening of the arteries.

Not every statement is useful as evidence. "I admire adults who exercise regularly" might be true, but it is a personal opinion that other people cannot prove or disprove using evidence.

Reasons include logical conclusions from evidence or ideas. For example, based on the statement by the Mayo Clinic, you could logically conclude that people who want to avoid hardening of the arteries should eat a low-fat diet.

One common mistake people make using reasons is to overgeneralize. People make a broad statement based on the results of only a few examples. "My grandfather ate a high-fat diet and he lived to be 95; therefore, high-fat diets are healthy." Making a general statement based on one person's experience is not using good logic.

 Activity 2A Identifying Reasons and Evidence

In the following paragraph, underline one example of evidence. Place parentheses around one example of a reason.

> Our school should start a program to encourage students to help elderly people own pets. This would help the elderly and the students. The elderly would be healthier. Researchers found that senior citizens with pets go to the doctor 30 percent less often than do those who without pets. Young people would develop a friendship with someone who is part of an earlier generation. One result of this friendship is that students would appreciate how much the world has improved since "the good old days."

Web Site Suffixes

In a Web page address, the last three letters indicate what type of site it is:

- "com" for commercial sites such as businesses
- "org" for organizations such as churches and clubs
- "edu" for educational sites, including universities
- "gov" for government sites

Some "com" sites and some "org" sites emphasize trying to sell you a product or an idea. In general, "gov" and "edu" sites focus on providing information, so they are more reliable.

LESSON 3 INTERPRETING A SOURCE

When reading a source, you may see words that are new to you. You can often figure out the meaning of one word from the words around it. Based on the other words in the sentence, what does *peevish* mean?

> The *peevish* child refused to walk or answer questions or do anything her parents wanted her to do all afternoon.

Since the child "refused . . . to do anything her parents wanted," *peevish* seems to describe someone who is stubborn and uncooperative.

Often, you can figure out the meaning of a word by what it is the opposite of. What does the word *capricious* mean in this sentence?

> While most teachers enforced their classroom rules consistently and predictably, Mr. Garza was *capricious.*

"While" suggests that Mr. Garza is the opposite of other teachers. Since other teachers act "consistently and predictably," *capricious* must mean inconsistent and unpredictable.

Check the Definition

To check that you understand the meaning of a new word correctly, look it up in a dictionary. The dictionary entry can also help you pronounce the word properly.

Activity 3A Explaining Words

Use the source to answer the questions about the meaning of inundate *and how you could figure it out from other words around it.*

Source 1

Record high tides inundate West Coast, hinting rough future of flooding as climate change boosts sea level

by David Knowles

More than 100 homes in west Seattle were hammered Monday. With sea levels on the rise worldwide, officials are grappling with the question of how to combat the ever-encroaching waters.

Source: Knowles, David. "Record High Tides." *Daily News.* 20 December 2012. Web. 14 March 2013. <nydailynews.com>

Part A
Circle the letter before the choice that best explains the meaning of inundate *in this passage.*

a. to predict the events

b. to destroy completely

c. to cover with water

d. to confront a problem

Part B
Circle the letters of the two words that work together to support your answer to Part A.

a. tides   b. rough   c. future   d. flooding

Identifying the Key Idea

A source usually includes one key idea. All of the other information should provide examples or help clarify this point. What is the key idea of this passage?

> Flooding on the Mississippi River is becoming a bigger problem. According to Robert Criss, a professor of Earth and planetary sciences at Washington University in Saint Louis, "Flooding is getting more frequent and more severe." Scientists are studying the data about floods and climate change to help them predict what will happen in the future.

The first sentence states the key idea: "Flooding on the Mississippi River is becoming a bigger problem." The next two sentences provide support for the point made in the first one.

Finding the Key Idea

The key idea of a paragraph is often stated in the first or the last sentence. The key idea in an essay is usually stated in the first or last paragraph.

Activity 3B Recognizing the Key Idea

Read the passage and answer the two questions about the key idea that follow the passage.

Source 2

Hurricane Sandy Flooding

by Ian Frazier

On October 29, 2012, a massive hurricane struck the northeastern United States. This excerpt describes the storm's impact.

Four days after the storm, I drove to Staten Island from my house in New Jersey to see some people I know. . . . When I got there, the street was about ten feet shorter. A fire hydrant dangled by its pipe in empty air, pieces of pavement crumbled downward, the traffic barrier and the sign saying "End" had washed away, and the house's lawn had been eaten back. Just down from the lawn, the enlarged beach was muddy and raw, and filled with so much debris that I put off looking at it until later. The house still stood, with plywood on the windows."

Source: Frazier, Ian. "Toll." *New Yorker.* February 11 and 18, 2013. Pages 38–39. Print.

Part A

Circle the letter before the choice that best states the key idea in "Hurricane Sandy Flooding."

a. The writer's friends were not injured by the storm.

b. Fire hydrants, traffic barriers, and signs are poorly made.

c. The larger beach was one benefit of the storm.

d. The storm caused tremendous damage.

Part B

Circle the letters before the two statements from "Hurricane Sandy Flooding" that best support your answer to Part A.

a. "I drove to Staten Island from my house in New Jersey"

b. "When I got there"

c. "pieces of pavement crumbled downward"

d. "Just down from the lawn"

e. "the enlarged beach was muddy and raw"

f. "The house still stood, with plywood on its windows"

©Perfection Learning® • No Reproduction Permitted.

LESSON 4 HOW TO WRITE AN ARGUMENTATIVE ESSAY

A good argumentative essay will show all of the traits of good writing described in Chapter 1. Keep these traits in mind as you advance step-by-step through the process of writing an argumentative essay.

Step 1. Analyze the prompt.

The directions for writing an essay are called the **prompt.** The prompt tells you the topic to write about and how to write about it.

Word in the Prompt	What Your Essay Should Do
Analyze the cause	Explain why something happened
Compare and contrast	Write about how two topics are similar and different
Describe	Identify details about the topic
Evaluate	Make a judgment about the topic
Recommend	State an action you think should be taken

Verbs in the Prompt

Students commonly focus only on the topic of a prompt and pay little attention to the verb in it. In a small group, discuss how these verbs that often appear in prompts differ from each other:

- Argue
- Explain
- Classify
- Infer
- Defend
- Judge
- Estimate
- Predict

Activity 4A Analyzing a Prompt

In the following prompt, underline the key phrase that identifies the topic. Place parentheses around five to ten words that tell you what to do with the topic.

> Trains built the United States. Heavy investment in railroads in the 1800s and early 1900s provided an efficient way to move goods and people around the country. Some of this investment was supported by money from the federal government. Write a claim stating whether or not you think the government should use tax money to help pay for improving train transportation today by funding fast-moving, energy-efficient "high-speed rail" lines. Provide evidence and reasons to support your claim.

Step 2. Takes notes on your sources.

On a test that provides you sources to use, read the sources and make notes about the information. Underline key ideas and details, and make notes in the margin that will help you address the prompt above.

Activity 4B Annotating Sources

Annotate the following sources for use in an essay in response to the prompt on the previous page.

Source 1

High Speed Rail Creates Jobs

The following excerpt is by the Federal Railroad Administration, the government agency that oversees railroads throughout the country.

The American Recovery and Reinvestment Act of 2009 (ARRA) and annual appropriations have provided $10.1 billion to expand passenger rail access to new communities and provide Americans with faster and more energy-efficient travel options. These investments are part of the Administration's plan to transform travel in America through targeted investments in five key mega-regions around the country, including a total of 34 states and the District of Columbia.

   With construction already underway or complete in 14 states, these projects will create tens of thousands of jobs, improve mobility, and stimulate American manufacturing. Through these initial investments and more to come in the future, the Administration, in coordination with the states and Amtrak, is working toward developing a passenger rail network that will connect 80 percent of Americans to high-speed rail in 25 years. . . .

   [The government will provide] $1.9 billion to expand high-speed rail service in the Midwest. Newly constructed segments of 110-mph track between Chicago, IL and Detroit, MI will save passengers 30 minutes in travel time and create nearly 1,000 new jobs in the construction phase. Upgrades to the Chicago, IL to St. Louis, MO corridor and 96 new miles of track will shave time off the trip, enhance safety and increase ridership. An estimated 5,000 jobs are expected to be created through the Chicago-St. Louis improvements alone.

Source: U.S. Department of Transportation. Federal Railroad Administration. Web. 14 March 2013.

©Perfection Learning® • No Reproduction Permitted.

Source 2

The Choice of Young People

by Joseph C. Szabo of the Federal Railroad Administration

It has been said that America has too much of a car culture to embrace trains. But, over the last eight years, Americans have actually driven less, while using passenger rail and public transit in record numbers. And it's important to understand that these patterns are shifting fastest among young people—who in an eight-year period starting in 2001 reduced their average vehicle miles traveled by 23 percent and increased their average miles traveled by rail and buses by a whopping 40 percent. Amtrak has set ridership records in nine of the last 10 years, with ridership growing close to 50 percent since 2000.

Source: Speech delivered on January 13, 2013, in Washington, D.C. Web. 14 March 213.

Source 3

Opposition to High-Speed Rail

from the Office of Congressional Representative Jeff Denham

U.S. Representative Jeff Denham (R-Turlock [California]), member of the House Transportation and Infrastructure Committee, today called on U.S. Department of Transportation Secretary Ray LaHood to address growing concerns regarding the viability of the proposed California project in the Administration's high-speed rail program during a House Committee hearing. "There are a lot of things we would like in California, and a new shiny train would be one of them," said Denham, Chairman of the Economic Development, Public Buildings and Emergency Management Subcommittee. "It would be fun to have, but the question you have to ask yourself is 'can we afford to have something fun, can we afford to have a luxury right now, and can we afford to do it with no viable plan and no private investment?'"

Source: Congressional Office of Representative Jeff Denham. December 6, 2012. Web. 14 March 2013.

Step 3. Organize your ideas.

To help you get your ideas in order, write a brief outline using standard outline form.

- Identify three to six main topics of your essay. Label them with Roman numerals. Usually the first topic is your introduction and the last topic is your conclusion.

- Underneath each main topic, list subtopics. Label these with capital letters.

- Underneath each subtopic, list details. Label these with Arabic numerals.

In the sample outline, notice how indents show the relationships between main topics, subtopics, and details.

Sample Outline: Investments in High-Speed Rail

I. Introduction
   A. Trains have been important in history.
   B. The government should use tax money to help build a better rail system today.

II. Body
   A. Building trains will create jobs throughout the country.
   B. High-speed rail provides energy efficient transportation.
   C. Young people want to travel by train.
      1. Young people drive less and take trains more.
      2. Three-fourths of young people are likely to travel by high-speed rail.
   D. Representative Denham opposes high-speed rail.
      1. He calls the proposal a "luxury."
      2. The proposal is not well planned.

III. Conclusion
   A. We need critics to be sure that the plans are practical.
   B. High-speed rails might be too risky for a private company, so government is a better way to try it.

Introduce the Claim

The first paragraph should capture the reader's attention with a surprising comment or fact. In addition, the first paragraph should state the claim clearly, often as the last sentence.

Organize the Support

Present the support for the claim in a clear order so the reader can follow it easily. For example, you might present the support according to when events happened, where events took place, or in the order of importance.

Provide a Strong Closing

The final paragraph should follow from the argument presented in the earlier paragraphs. It should summarize the key points already made.

©Perfection Learning® • No Reproduction Permitted.

Step 4. Write the draft.

Use your notes and your outline to help you write an essay. The following sample draft includes mistakes that you will correct in later activities.

Writing a First Draft Quickly

Some writers have trouble writing a first draft because they try to make every word exactly right the first time. Many successful writers write a first draft quickly and then revise it carefully.

Sample Draft: High-Speed Rail

Railroads existed in the United States in the 1800s. They attached this nation together, just as railroads did in other countries. A new high-speed rail system could be as useful as the old system. Fast-moving trains could give people a choice so they do not have to take planes or cars everywhere. Today, the government should use money on a high-speed rail system, even if that means rasing taxs.

In addition, building a high-speed rail system will create jobs. Fixing old railroads, building new ones, and manufacturing new train engines will be jobs that people need. According to a statement by the Federal Railroad Administration (FRA), building a high speed railroad between Chicago and Detroit will create 1,000 new jobs. In the same statement, the FRA estimated that improving the railroad connecting Chicago and St. Louis will create 5,000 jobs.

Critics say that the current plans for high-speed railroads are a bad idea. California Representative Jeff Denham asks, "Can we afford to have a luxury right now?" He charges that there is "no viable plan and no private investment" in the high-speed rail business. However, the government has always taken on tasks that are too big and risky for private companies to try. The government gave railroads subsidies. It paid for highways in the 1950s. It promoted the exploration of space. Today, space travel is cheap enough and safe enough that private companys are flying into space. Progress marchs on!

High-speed rails could have great benefits. In the future, they could create jobs in other industrys by making make travel faster and more energy efficient. Now, they themselfs could create jobs. High-speed rail might be risky, but the government should invest in it.

Citations

In some writing assignments, you will need to identify your sources in your text. For examples showing how to do this, see page 46.

Step 5. Revise your essay.

After you write the first draft of your essay, read it. Replace words, phrases, and sentences with ones that express your thoughts and attitudes more precisely and more clearly.

For example, in the last sentence of the first paragraph of the sample, the writer urges the government to "use money." Instead of "use," the writer could have said *invest* or *squander*. All three words have the same **denotation,** or basic meaning.

However, these words have different **nuances,** or small differences. These differences produce a word's connotation. A **connotation** is the additional emotions of a word associated with it. *Invest* means to use money wisely. *Squander* means to waste it. Choosing words with accurate connotations will give your writing the tone that you want to express.

Technology and Precise Words

Word processing programs often include a thesaurus and a dictionary. The thesaurus can suggest words with a similar meaning to one you have entered. The dictionary can give you precise definitions of words you are not familiar with.

Activity 4C Identifying Connotations

Underline the word in each pair that you would use to praise someone.

1. old, experienced
2. cheerful, silly
3. energetic, out-of-control
4. polite, untruthful
5. mean, honest
6. focused, boring

Collaboration on Nuance

In a small group, make a list of ten words. For each word, list two others that have a similar denotation. As a group discuss the distinctive connotation of each.

Activity 4D Using Connotations

Replace each underlined word in this excerpt from the sample with a word that has that same denotation, but a connotation that expresses the view of the writer more precisely. Write your words on the lines below.

Railroads <u>existed in</u> the United States in the 1800s. They <u>attached</u> this nation together, just as railroads did in other countries. A <u>new</u> high-speed rail system could be as useful as the old system.

1. existed in _____

2. attached _____

3. new _____

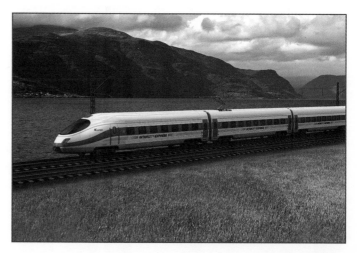

©Perfection Learning® • No Reproduction Permitted.

Use Phrases and Clauses

As you revise your essay, insert descriptions, examples, and other details by adding phrases and clauses to your sentences.

- A **phrase** is a group of words that acts as a single part of speech, such as an adverb or an adjective.
- A **clause** is a group of words that has a subject and a verb. If a clause expresses a complete thought, it can stand alone as a sentence.

Compare the italicized groups of words in these two sentences:

We will eat *after the lessons.*

We will eat *after we finish our lessons.*

In the first sentence, *after the lessons* is a phrase that serves as an adverb because it tells when something will happen. In the second sentence, *after we finish our lessons* also tells when something will happen. Since it includes a noun *(we)* and a verb *(finish)* it is a clause.

You can use both phrases and clauses to strengthen your writing by making it more detailed. For example, you can

- specify which one or what kind of item you are describing
- express precisely how, when, where, to what extent, or why something happened

> ### Adjectives and Adverbs
>
> An **adjective** is a word that modifies a noun or pronoun. It answers the questions:
>
> - What kind?
> - Which one?
> - How many?
> - How much?
>
> An **adverb** is a word that modifies a verb, an adjective, or another adverb. It answers the questions:
>
> - Where?
> - When?
> - How?
> - Why?
>
> Adverbs often end in -ly. Examples: quickly, lively, and bravely.

Activity 4E Identifying Phrases and Clauses

Circle the number before each sentence in which the group of words in italics is a clause.

1. *The sky is dark and cloudy,* so you should bring an umbrella.

2. We need a hotel room *with two beds.*

3. The snail crawled *at a slow pace.*

4. Since the tide is in, *the water is high.*

5. The shoe, *the one with the black sole,* belongs to my brother.

6. *Someone knocked on the door* as soon as I got home.

7. I read another story *that I like.*

8. He waited *because of the terrible storm.*

Activity 4F Using Phrases and Clauses

Use information from Source 1, "High Speed Rail" to rewrite this passage, adding phrases or clauses to answer each of the questions in parentheses.

Construction (where?) will employ many thousands of people. (When?) about 80 percent of Americans could have high speed rail. The Chicago-Detroit train will go fast, (how fast?).

_____

_____

_____

_____

_____

_____

Step 6. Edit and proofread your essay.

After you have revised your essay, read it again very carefully. Check the spelling, grammar, and punctuation.

To spell the plural of most nouns, simply add an *s*. The most common exceptions include:

- If a noun ends in *s, ch, sh, x,* or *z,* add *es*. Example: box, boxes.
- If a noun ends in a consonant and *y,* change the *y* to *i* and add *es*. Example: hobby, hobbies.
- For some nouns that end in *f* or *fe,* change the *f* or *fe* to *v* and add *es*. Example: half, halves.

Activity 4G Spelling Plural Nouns

Below are ten plural nouns used in the sample. If it is spelled correctly, write "correct" on the blank. If not, write the correct spelling.

1. railroads _____

2. countrys _____

3. trains _____

4. planes _____

5. taxs _____

6. companys _____

7. industrys _____

8. themselfs _____

9. marchs _____

10. subsidies _____

Catching Misspelled Words

The human brain makes catching misspelled words challenging. Can you understand this sentence?

A hmuan mnid raeds eahc wrdo as a wlohe, nto lteter by letetr.

Spelled correctly, the sentence reads:

A human mind reads each word as a whole, not letter by letter.

©Perfection Learning® • No Reproduction Permitted.

LESSON 5 YOU TRY IT

Now it is your turn to write an argumentative essay. Use what you learned in this chapter about claims, evidence, and reasons. Follow the steps outlined in the last lesson. They are also listed below.

Step 1. Analyze the prompt.

Step 2. Take notes on the sources.

Step 3. Organize your ideas.

Step 4. Write the draft.

Step 5. Revise your essay.

Step 6. Edit and proofread your essay.

Activity 5A Writing an Argumentative Essay

Write an argumentative essay in response to one of these prompts.

Publish on the Internet

When you complete an argumentative essay, look for a Web site where you can publish your work. Some sites specialize in particular topics. Others focus on the work of school students. If your essay is about a local issue, check community news sites.

A. Advertisements in Schools	B. Learning Penmanship
One way schools can raise money is by selling advertisements. Write a two- to four-page argumentative essay about whether you think schools should have any limits on the advertising they can sell. Support your claim with information from at least three sources.	Since people today commonly write using a keyboard, many schools devote less time to teaching penmanship than they used to. Write a two- to four-page argumentative essay about whether elementary schools should teach cursive writing. Support your claim with information from at least three sources.

Checklist

Use the following checklist to revise and edit your essay.

	My writing has . . .
DEVELOPMENT	❏ a clear central claim ❏ strong supporting evidence ❏ one or more counterclaims
ORGANIZATION	❏ a clear introduction, body, and conclusion ❏ good transitions ❏ logical order
EVIDENCE	❏ strong, relevant textual evidence ❏ enough evidence to be convincing
LANGUAGE & STYLE	❏ precise, appropriate word choice ❏ a formal, objective tone
GRAMMAR, SPELLING, & PUNCTUATION	❏ standard grammar ❏ correct spelling ❏ proper punctuation

Writing an Informative Essay

An **informative/explanatory essay,** also called just an informative essay, explains or provides information about a topic. Examples of informative writing range from describing the living conditions at summer camp to explaining the rules for a game.

LESSON 1 THESIS STATEMENT

You want your reader to know the purpose of your informative essay. A **thesis statement** should clearly state the central idea of an essay. A good thesis statement should be

- clear and precise
- based upon the requirements of the prompt
- based upon the texts you were asked to read or view

Compare these three thesis statements for an informative essay on the movie *The Wizard of Oz.*

A. Dorothy learns a lot of lessons through different experiences.

B. Dorothy goes through lots of changes as she learns about ideas such as why friends are important and why families are also important.

C. Dorothy discovers the value of loyal friends and a loving family.

Notice how vague A is and how wordy B is. C is the best thesis statement because it is clearer and more precise than the other two.

> ### Phrases to Avoid in Thesis Statements
>
> State your thesis without wasted words. Do not begin it with "My main idea is" or with "In this essay I will."

 ### Activity 1A *Making a Thesis Statement Precise*

Rewrite each thesis statement to make it clearer and more precise.

Thesis Statement	Revision
1. The structure of the atom that we study in science class shows the way that protons, neutrons, electrons, and lots of other particles are connected to each other.	
2. Some movies say something about some trends today.	
3. The series of books about Harry Potter show how he and his friends change.	

    ©Perfection Learning® • No Reproduction Permitted.

LESSON 2 SUPPORT FOR THE THESIS STATEMENT

You should support your thesis statement with details. Some examples of details are facts, examples, incidents, analogies, causes, and effects. Strong supporting details are relevant. **Relevant** details are ones directly related to the thesis statement. Consider this thesis statement:

> In the United States, the percentage of the population legally allowed to vote has increased since 1788.

Which of these details is more relevant to the above thesis statement?

A. The Nineteenth Amendment, which gives women the right to vote, was ratified in 1920.

B. In a typical presidential election, between 55 percent and 65 percent of people who were legally allowed to vote cast votes.

The first detail is very relevant because it describes a legal change that increased the percentage of people who could vote. The second detail is not as relevant because it focuses on who chooses to vote, not who is legally allowed to.

Activity 2A *Identifying Supporting Details*

Place a check mark in the correct column in each row to indicate whether the statement is relevant to this thesis statement:

> In the United States, the percentage of the population legally allowed to vote has increased since 1788.

Statement	Relevant	Not Relevant
1. The Fifteenth Amendment, ratified in 1867, was designed to protect the rights of African Americans to vote.		
2. Four presidents have been elected even though they did not win the popular vote.		
3. In 1893, New Zealand became the first government to allow women to vote throughout the country.		
4. In the early days of the United States, several states allowed only people who owned property to vote.		
5. In general, the percentage of people who vote is higher in years with a presidential election than in years without one.		

©Perfection Learning® • No Reproduction Permitted.

The Purpose of Informative Writing

When choosing supporting details, keep in mind that your purpose is to examine your topic and to convey information. You are not concerned with presenting an argument.

Collaboration on Details

Talking before you write often helps you identify what you want to say and helps you clarify how to say it. When working on an essay, discuss the topic with a friend to identify what details would be most useful to include.

LESSON 3 ANALYZING SOURCES

Your informative essays will usually be based on facts and reasons that you have gathered by reading texts closely. Sometimes you will use just a few important points from a text in your essay. Often you will use a summary of a source. A **summary** is a shorter version of a text that includes the key idea and the most important supporting details.

Activity 3A *Writing a Summary*

Write a summary of the following text on the lines provided. The Soviet Union was a country that existed between 1922 and 1991. It included Russia and regions surrounding it. Soviet astronauts were known as cosmonauts.

> ### Types of Sources
>
> Sources can be of several types:
>
> - informational texts, such as news reports
> - literary texts, such as novels or poems
> - multimedia texts, such as videos
> - visual texts, such as graphs or paintings

Early in the morning of April 12, 1961, 27-year-old [Soviet] Air Force cosmonaut [Yuri] Gagarin boarded a small bus for the . . . launchpad . . . . Just over two hours remained until the Soviet Union would attempt to launch *Vostok 1* and make Major Gagarin the first man in outer space. If Gagarin was nervous about this momentous—and perilous—journey, he did not show it. Like other cosmonauts and astronauts who would follow him into space, Gagarin faced the great unknown that lay before him with equanimity and a sense of humor. During the bus ride to the launch site, he was the one keeping the physicians, technicians, military officers, and fellow cosmonauts who accompanied him from becoming too somber or worried. Just before arriving at the pad, he invited everybody to join him in a song (they declined).

Source: Gregory P. Kennedy. *The First Men in Space.* New York: Chelsea House Publishers. 1991.

    ©Perfection Learning® • No Reproduction Permitted.

LESSON 4 HOW TO WRITE AN INFORMATIVE ESSAY

Following is a model demonstrating eight steps in writing an informative essay. Use these steps to help you write on your own.

Step 1. Analyze the prompt.

The directions for writing an essay are called the **prompt**. By reading the prompt closely, you will understand precisely what you are expected to write. Below is an example of a prompt.

> Asthma is a common condition marked by difficulty breathing. Write an informative essay in which you describe asthma and its possible causes. Use evidence from the texts provided.

 ### Activity 4A *Analyzing the Prompt*

Explain in your own words what "describe" means in the above prompt.

Step 2. Take notes on sources.

Keep the prompt in mind as you read the sources closely and take notes on them. For more on annotating, see page 10.

 ### Activity 4B *Annotating Sources*

Annotate the following sources to prepare to write an essay in response to the prompt in Step 1 above.

Source 1

Asthma: The Basics

Asthma is so common that almost everyone has a friend or relative with it. People with asthma have periods when they have difficulty getting a full breath. They wheeze or cough, and their chest feels tight. Usually, these periods are triggered by something they breathe in, such as cigarette smoke. For others, it is dust, so they have trouble in hot, dry climates. Some people are sensitive to molds, so damp, decaying leaves in the autumn can cause their asthma to act up. Others react to animal dander. In addition, some people have exercise-induced asthma. For these people, vigorous activity sets off their asthma. Most people can control their asthma with medication they take through an inhaler.

Gathering Information with Technology

A bibliography is a list of sources about a specific topic. If you need more sources to choose from, do a search using your topic and the word *bibliography*. For example, a search for "asthma bibliography" might find bibliographies produced by public libraries that focus on materials written for students.

©Perfection Learning® • No Reproduction Permitted.

Source 2

Asthma's Impact on the Nation

An estimated 29.1 million adults (12.7 percent) have been diagnosed with asthma in their lifetimes, and 18.7 million (8.2 percent) still had asthma, according to 2010 data from the Centers for Disease Control and Prevention. The report, *Asthma's Impact on the Nation,* is the first state-by-state data gathered using the Asthma Call-back Survey, an in-depth survey conducted among people with asthma identified by the CDC Behavioral Risk Factor Surveillance System.

"The information in this release is a stark reminder that asthma continues to be a major public health concern with a large financial impact on families, the nation, and our health care system," said Christopher J. Portier, Ph.D., director of CDC's National Center for Environmental Health and the Agency for Toxic Substances and Disease Registry. . . .

In 2010, an estimated 10.1 million (13.6 percent) children had been diagnosed with asthma in their lifetimes, and 7.0 million (9.4 percent) still had asthma. During 2001–2010, the proportion of persons with asthma in the United States increased by 14.8 percent.

In 2008, children aged 5–17 years who had one or more asthma attacks in the previous 12 months missed 10.5 million days of school. Adults who were currently employed and had one or more asthma attacks during the previous 12 months missed 14.2 million days of work due to asthma. In 2009, asthma accounted for 3,388 deaths, 479,300 hospitalizations, 1.9 million emergency department (ED) visits, and 8.9 million physician office visits. . . .

Source: Adapted from "Survey Reveals Growing National Impact of Asthma." Centers for Disease Control and Prevention. 3 May 2011. Web. 23 March 2013. <cdc.gov>

     ©Perfection Learning® • No Reproduction Permitted.

Source 3

The Global Burden of Asthma

1. Asthma is one of the most common chronic diseases in the world. It is estimated that around 300 million people in the world currently have asthma. . . .

2. The international patterns of asthma prevalence are not explained by the current knowledge of the causation of asthma. . . .

3. Asthma has become more common in both children and adults around the world in recent decades. . . .

4. The rate of asthma increases as communities adopt western lifestyles and become urbanised. . . . [There] may be an additional 100 million persons with asthma by 2025.

Source: "Global Burden of Asthma." Global Initiative for Asthma.Web. 23 Mar 2013. <inasthma.org>

Source 4

How Asthma-Friendly Is Your School?

The federal government helps schools evaluate how well they support students with asthma.

Are the school buildings and grounds free of tobacco smoke at all times? Are all school buses, vans, and trucks free of tobacco smoke? Are all school events, like field trips and team games (both "at-home" and "away"), free from tobacco smoke?

Does your school have a policy or rule that allows students to carry and use their own asthma medicines? If some students do not carry their asthma medicines, do they have quick and easy access to their medicines?

Does your school have a written emergency plan for teachers and staff to follow to take care of a student who has an asthma attack? In an emergency, such as a fire, weather, or lockdown, or if a student forgets his/her medicine, does your school have standing orders and quick-relief medicines for students to use?

Source: National Institutes of Health. October 2008. Web. 23 March 2013. <nih.gov>

Step 3. Write a thesis statement.

Once you have gathered some ideas that you want to include in your essay, you can write a thesis statement. Include your thesis statement in the introduction to your essay. It will guide you as you decide which ideas to include in the body of your paper.

Activity 4C Writing a Thesis Statement

Based upon your notes, write a thesis statement for your essay.

_____

_____

_____

_____

Domain-Specific Vocabulary

Each topic you study will have its own special terms. For instance, *inhaler* is a common word in medical texts, but not elsewhere. *Inhaler* is an example of **domain-specific vocabulary,** words used in a specific content area. Use a glossary or dictionary to help you learn these terms.

Step 4. Organize your ideas.

After you have read and annotated your sources, figure out the best order in which to present your idea. Select a logical order so that readers can easily follow your ideas. Some possible ways to organize an essay on an astronomy topic are listed below:

Type of Organization	Method	Example
Definition	• Clarify the definition of key terms	What is a black hole?
Classification	• Describe larger categories that include the topic • Describe smaller components that make up the topic	Is Pluto a planet?
Comparison/Contrast	• Identify similarities • Identify differences	How is Mars like and unlike Venus?
Cause/Effect	• Describe how events lead to others • Describe how events result from others	How does gravity causes tides on Earth?
Scope	• Present information from the smallest to the largest category • Present information from the largest to the smallest category	How does the size of a star influence its other characteristics?

©Perfection Learning® • No Reproduction Permitted.

Technology and Graphic Organizers

One way to help you organize your ideas is with a graphic organizer. A search for "graphic organizers" will result in several examples.

Activity 4D Using Strategies for Organization

Write a question about asthma or another topic of your choice that you could answer using the type of organization identified.

1. Definition

_____

_____

2. Classification

_____

_____

3. Comparison/Contrast

_____

_____

4. Cause/Effect

_____

_____

5. Scope

_____

_____

Step 5. Develop a complete outline.

Organize your information in standard outline form. You should include an introduction, body, and conclusion. For more details on creating an outline, see page 22.

Activity 4E Completing an Outline

Fill in the blanks in the outline using information from the sources.

Sample Outline: Asthma

Thesis: Asthma affects individuals, the country, and the world.

I.   Introduction

  A. Asthma is_____.

  B. Asthma affects individuals, the country, and the world.

II. The Impact of Asthma

  A. Asthma is hard on individuals.

   1. Asthma can make _____ difficult.

   2. Asthma can be triggered by_____

    _____

   3. Asthma can be triggered by exercise.

   4. Schools should have policies to help students with asthma.

    a. Schools should keep their air clean.

    b. _____

  B. Asthma is costly to the United States.

   1. Over _____ percent of children have asthma.

   2. Between 2001 and 2010, the number of people with

    asthma increased by _____ percent.

  C. Asthma is a global problem.

   1. "Asthma is one of the most common chronic diseases in the

    world," according to _____.

   2. Rates of asthma increase as people live more like
    Americans.

III. Conclusion

  A. Asthma is widespread.

  B. Asthma can be controlled.

Step 6. Write the draft.

Using your notes and your outline, write your essay. A sample draft of an essay is shown next. It includes errors you will correct later. In some assignments, you will need to cite the sources for your statements. For examples showing how to do this, see page 46.

     ©Perfection Learning® • No Reproduction Permitted.

Sample Draft: Asthma

You just did it. And you just did it again—and maybe again already. Without thinking, breathing comes naturally. However, breathing for a person with asthma can be difficult. Asthma is a chronic condition that causes people to wheeze and cough. It is a serious medical problem for individuals, the country, and the world.

The Individual

Asthma is hard on every, single individual who has it because it sometimes makes breathing difficult. A trigger, such as smoke, dust, mold, or pet dander, can set it off. For some people, vigorous, energetic exercise is a trigger. Schools can set up reasonable, practical policies to help students control their asthma. For example, schools should keep their air clean. Considerate, school leaders should prohibit all smoking on school property. In addition, students should be allowed to keep their inhalers. Schools with strict written policies on medicines should make exceptions for students with asthma. The federal government has a list of questions schools can ask themselves to review their policies.

The Country

So many individuals have asthma that the condition is an important problem for the country. Over 9 percent of children have asthma. The percentage is growing. Between 2001 and 2010, the number of people with asthma increased by almost 15 percent. While most people can control their asthma with medication, not all can. Sometimes asthma is serious.

The World

The problems of asthma go beyond the United States. According to the Global Initiative for Asthma, "Asthma is one of the most common chronic diseases in the world." The disease is likely to increase in the future.

Asthma is important. It makes life hard for individuals. It affects almost one out of ten students. It is widespread in the world, and becoming more common. With medication, though, people can control it and breath easily. Think about that next time you breath.

Activity 4F Analyzing a Draft

In the margin of the draft, mark the following:

1. Write a note beside the introduction evaluating whether you think it draws the reader in.

2. Underline the main topic of the second, third, and fourth paragraphs.

3. Place a star beside two places where the thesis is stated.

4. Write brief notes beside places in the third and fourth paragraphs where the writer could add details to strengthen a point.

Step 7. Revise your essay.

After you write a draft, read it again. Correct any misplaced modifiers. A **misplaced modifier** is a word, phrase, or clause that does not clearly describe the word the writer intended it to. Often, moving the modifier closer to the word it describes clarifies the meaning.

Misplaced Modifiers	Problem	Properly Placed Modifiers
The teacher gave the popcorn to the children *without butter or salt.*	Which lacked butter and salt, the popcorn or the children?	The teacher gave the popcorn *without butter or salt* to the children.
Drinking a soda, the gorilla watched Tim.	Who was drinking a soda, the gorilla or Tim?	The gorilla watched Tim *drinking a soda.*
I *only yelled at* Joe.	What is the speaker denying, hitting Joe or yelling at other people?	I *yelled at only* Joe.

Activity 4G Placing Modifiers Correctly

The first paragraph of the sample essay includes two sentences with misplaced modifiers. Rewrite them with the modifiers placed correctly.

1. _____

   _____

   _____

2. _____

   _____

   _____

   _____

Dangling Modifiers

A modifier that describes a word that is not in the sentence is called a **dangling modifier.** For example: "After hearing Kendra, the newspaper seemed wrong." The phrase "After hearing Kendra" describes the speaker, who is not mentioned in the sentence.

The sentence should be: "After hearing Kendra, I thought the newspaper seemed wrong."

Step 8. Edit and proofread your essay.

After you finish revising your essay, read it again very carefully to catch and correct any mistakes in grammar, punctuation, and spelling. For example, check whether you need a comma to separate two adjectives before a noun by mentally inserting *and* between the two adjectives.

- If sentence reads well with *and,* insert a comma.

  Monday was a warm, humid night.

  "Monday was a warm and humid night" sounds natural because *warm* and *humid* modify *night* in a similar way.

- It the sentence does not read well with *and,* do not use a comma.

  Monday was a warm baseball night.

  "Monday was a warm and baseball night" sounds awkward because *warm* and *baseball* modify *night* in quite different ways.

Activity 4H Using Commas Between Adjectives

Below is the second paragraph of the sample essay. If a sentence includes a comma that should be omitted, cross it out with an X. If a sentence is missing a comma, add one and circle it.

Asthma is hard on every, single individual who has it because it sometimes makes breathing difficult. A trigger, such as smoke, dust, mold, or pet dander, can set it off. For some people, vigorous energetic exercise is a trigger. Schools can set up reasonable practical policies to help students control their asthma. For example, schools should keep their air clean. Considerate, school leaders should prohibit all smoking on school property. In addition, students should be allowed to keep their inhalers. Schools with strict written policies on medicines should make exceptions for students with asthma.

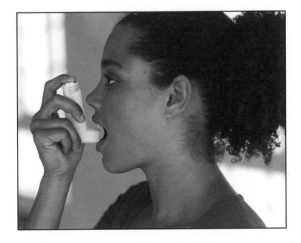

> **Coordinate Adjectives**
>
> Adjectives are words that modify a noun. If two adjectives modify a noun in a similar way, they are called **coordinate adjectives.**

> **Technology and Revisions**
>
> Word processing programs often underline words they do not recognize. These words might be misspelled. However, they might be spelled correctly, but just not in the program's dictionary.
>
> This most often happens with personal names or special term. If you have words that you use often that the program does not recognize, see if you can add them to the dictionary used by the word processor.

LESSON 5 YOU TRY IT

Now it is your turn to write an informative essay using what you have learned in this chapter. Follow these steps:

Step 1. Analyze the prompt.   **Step 5.** Develop a complete outline.

Step 2. Take notes on the sources.   **Step 6.** Write the draft.

Step 3. Write a thesis statement.   **Step 7.** Revise your essay.

Step 4. Organize your ideas.   **Step 8.** Edit and proofread your essay.

Activity 5A *Writing an Informative Essay*

Write an informative essay in response to one of the following prompts. Use information from at least three sources.

A. Analyzing Aquaculture	B. Vending Machines in Schools
For thousands of years, people have raised fish and other water animals for food. In the past six decades, though, aquaculture has dramatically increased in importance. Write a two- to four-page argumentative essay about whether the expansion of aquaculture is beneficial. Support your claim with information from at least three sources.	Write an informative essay explaining the costs and the benefits of having vending machines in schools that sell candy and soda pop. Your essay should be two to four pages long. You should refer to specific evidence from your research in your essay.

Checklist

Use the following checklist to revise and edit your essay.

My writing has . . .	
DEVELOPMENT	❑ a clear thesis ❑ strong supporting points ❑ relevant information based upon research
ORGANIZATION	❑ a clear introduction, body, and conclusion ❑ good transitions ❑ logical order
EVIDENCE	❑ strong, relevant textual evidence ❑ direct and indirect quotations
LANGUAGE & STYLE	❑ precise, appropriate word choice ❑ a formal, objective tone
GRAMMAR, SPELLING, & PUNCTUATION	❑ standard grammar ❑ correct spelling ❑ proper punctuation

   ©Perfection Learning® • No Reproduction Permitted.

Reporting on Research

In a research report, you gather information from multiple sources to help you answer a question. This process of combining information from different sources into one report is called **synthesizing.**

LESSON 1 QUESTIONS FOR RESEARCH

The question you want to answer might be given to you by a teacher or on a test. Or it might be one that you want to find out about for yourself. A good question is

- broad enough that you can easily find several sources about it
- narrow enough that you can cover it in the time and space you have available for researching and writing
- phrased fairly so that you can analyze it from many points of view

Often, the first question you think of to research will be too big to cover. You will need to narrow it down. Sometimes, you may start with a very narrow question that you decide you need to broaden.

Activity 1A Revising a Question

Following are possible questions for research reports. Assume you have two weeks to write a three-page report. After looking at the problem with each one, write a revised topic.

Topic	Problem	Revised Topic
1. How might cars change in the next fifty years?	Too broad	
2. How many cars are sold each year in the United States?	Too narrow	
3. Why are cars so bad for society?	Worded unfairly	

> **Collaborate and Revise Your Question**
>
> Talking with a friend about a question is a good way to decide if it is too broad or too narrow. Discuss possible sources and whether they are easily available. As you research, refocus your topic as you find new information.

LESSON 2 RELEVANT INFORMATION

Sources come in many forms. They can be literary sources from novels or short stories. They can be informational text, such as government reports or encyclopedia articles. They can be images, such as photographs or drawings. Whatever form your sources are in, they should be relevant and authoritative.

- **Relevant** sources are ones that include information you can use.
- **Authoritative** sources are ones produced by knowledgeable individuals that people trust.

Take notes from your sources so that you can remember the information accurately. Identify the source for each note so that you can find the original information again if you need to.

 ### Activity 2A Identifying Relevant Sources

In each item, indicate which news article sounds more relevant to a research report on the history of cell phones. Explain your choice.

1. A. "The First Cell Phone"
   B. "Doing Research by Cell Phone"

_____

_____

_____

_____

2. A. "Recent Improvements in Cell Phones"
   B. "Choosing the Best Cell Phone Provider"

_____

_____

_____

_____

3. A. "Comparing DTMF and Secode 2805 in Mobile Phones"
   B. "Cell Phones: A Short History"

_____

_____

_____

_____

Finding Relevant Sources

Many Web sites provide bibliographies of print and digital sources. Your teacher or a librarian can help you find a bibliography that is likely to include sources relevant for your topic.

©Perfection Learning® • No Reproduction Permitted.

Activity 2B Identifying Authoritative Sources

In each pair, select the one that is more authoritative about the history of cell phones. Explain your choice.

1. A. an article in an encyclopedia on technology
   B. a paragraph in a book of odd facts about inventions

   _____

   _____

   _____

   _____

2. A. a social media posting by an unnamed person
   B. an online lecture by a professor at a state university

   _____

   _____

   _____

   _____

3. A. a news report in a respected newspaper
   B. a television report on the cell phones used by celebrities

   _____

   _____

   _____

   _____

4. A. a Web site run by a United States government agency
   B. a Web site run by a manufacturer of cell phones

   _____

   _____

   _____

   _____

Evaluate Credibility

Evaluating the credibility, or trustworthiness, of sources is a good process to go through with classmates. You can help each other make reasoned judgments about how much to trust each source.

©Perfection Learning® • No Reproduction Permitted.

Activity 2C Interpreting Sources Accurately

Read the following passage and answer the questions that follow it.

The cellphone . . . a device that as recently as 1990 was an oddity, has long since reached ubiquity. Market saturation [the condition when every consumer who wants a product has purchased it] in the usual developed countries of North America and Europe approached or surpassed 100 percent at the turn of the century, meaning that some countries had more cellphones than people.

Source: Klemens, Guy. *The Cellphone: The History and Technology of the Gadget That Changed the World.* Jefferson, North Carolina: McFarland, 2010. Page 1.

Part A

Circle the letter before the sentence that best expresses the meaning of the phrase "long since reached ubiquity."

    a. Cellphones became outdated soon after they were invented.

    b. Cellphones have been common everywhere for many years.

    c. Cellphones are available only in wealthy countries.

    d. Cellphones outnumber people in undeveloped countries.

Part B

Circle the letter before the statement that best supports the correct meaning of ubiquity *in the phrase in Part A.*

    a. *ubiquity* is an older form of *oddity*

    b. *ubiquity* is a specific example of *oddity*

    c. *ubiquity* means something that causes *oddity*

    d. *ubiquity* means the opposite of *oddity*

> **Two-Part Questions**
> ....
> Tests may include questions about vocabulary or key ideas followed by a question that asks you to identify the evidence for the answer you provided. These questions may be labeled Part A and Part B.

©Perfection Learning® • No Reproduction Permitted.

LESSON 3 SYNTHESIS OF SOURCES

Research includes finding information in several sources and combining that information into one report. This process of combining parts into a new whole is called **synthesizing.** When you synthesize, you need to accurately express how one idea is connected to another.

- If one idea causes another, you could connect them with a word such as *hence, therefore,* or *consequently.* For example, notice how *as a result* connects the ideas in this sentence:

  The lock broke, and *as a result,* the gorilla escaped.

- If one idea supports another, you could connect them with a word such as *furthermore, accordingly, similarly, besides,* or *also.* Notice how *in addition* connects the facts in these sentences.

  During the 1990s, people began to describe stories of under 1,000 words as flash fiction. *In addition,* some people called these stories micro fiction or short short stories.

- If one idea limits or contradicts another, you could connect them using a word or phrase such as *however, nevertheless,* and *on the other hand.* Notice how *in contrast* tells readers that the second sentence will limit the meaning of the first one.

  Short stories are between 2,000 words and 15,000 words long. *In contrast,* flash fiction stories are usually under 1,000 words.

> **Cause and Effect**
>
> As you gather and synthesize information, identify causes and effects cautiously. For example, some people say that violent video games cause violence in society. Others say the opposite: the violence in society causes people to choose to play violent video games. If your sources disagree about a cause, either report them both or evaluate them to decide which one has stronger support.

Activity 3A Connecting and Contrasting

Fill in the blank in each sentence with a word that shows how the two phrases or sentences either support or limit each other.

1. I enjoy reading Edgar Allan Poe short stories, _____ my friend does not.

2. Anton Chekhov wrote wonderful short stories. _____, he also worked as a physician.

3. "The Lottery," by Shirley Jackson is well-written. _____, it is too terrifying for young children.

4. Jorge Luis Borges was much admired in his home country of Argentina, _____ the rest of the world.

5. I read "The Treasures of Lemon Brown" by Walter Dean Myers last summer. _____ we read it for class last fall.

Citations and Quotations

When you gather information from books, magazines, and Web sites, you should give credit to your sources. A **citation** is a note in a text that identifies the source of information. Usually, it includes the author's last name and the page number from the work. You can include this information in the text or in parentheses at the end of the sentence. Following is an excerpt about writer James Baldwin by Donald B. Gibson in *The Encyclopedia of American Biography,* pages 53–54:

> James Baldwin's progress toward religious conversion is vividly told in *Go Tell It on the Mountain* . . . Baldwin's religious conversion led him ultimately to become a minister at the age of 14. Though he later gave up the ministry, he did not give up his strong belief in Christian values, especially love and most other tenets [principles] of Christian morality.

Here are two ways to use information from this source:

- A **direct quotation** repeats part of a source word-for-word. The words that are taken from the source appear in quotation marks.

  According to Donald B. Gibson, James Baldwin "became a minister at the age of 14" (pp. 53–54).

- An **indirect quotation** uses information from a source, but not the exact words. An indirect quotation is also called a **paraphrase.**

  While yet a teenager, Balwin began to serve his community as a minister (Gibson, pp. 53–54).

Note that the author and page number are given in each example, either in the text or in parentheses at the end of the statement.

Activity 3B Using Citations and Quotations

1. Write a sentence that uses a direct quotation from the passage by Gibson to describe Baldwin's religious views. Include the author and page number in the sentence.

_____

_____

2. Write a sentence that uses an indirect quotation from Gibson to describe Baldwin's religious views. Include the author and page number in parentheses at the end of the sentence.

_____

_____

Plagiarism

Research involves collecting the ideas of others and synthesizing them into something new. This synthesis is very different from plagiarism. **Plagiarism** is presenting someone else's ideas as your own. You can avoid plagiarism by giving credit to your sources and by using quotation marks when you use someone else's words.

Works Cited List

At the end of a report, you should include a list of all the sources you used. This is called a Works Cited list. The entry for the book that includes the excerpt by Gibson would be as follows:

Gibson, Donald B. "James Baldwin." *The Encyclopedia of American Biography.* Ed. John A. Garraty. New York: Harper and Row, 1974. Pages 53–54. Print.

Greek and Latin Word Parts

In doing research, you will read words that are new to you. You could look each one up in a dictionary or try to figure out a word's meaning from its context. In addition, you could analyze the parts of the word. Imagine you see the sentence, "Juanita wanted to *circumvent* the problem with her parents." Assume that you do not know the meaning of *circumvent*, but you do know that

- *circumference* is "the distance around a circle"
- *venture* means "to travel"

You reason that *circum* might mean "around" and *vent* might mean "move," so *circumvent* could mean to move around something. You would be right.

You can break many words into smaller parts. The core part of a word is the **base word**. The part that comes before a base word is called a **prefix.** The part that comes after the base word is called a **suffix.** Many English base words, prefixes, and suffixes can be traced back to the Greek and Latin languages spoken over 2,000 years ago. The table below lists examples of Greek and Latin word parts.

Part	Use	Meaning	Examples
belli	base	war	belligerent, antebellum
viv or vita	base	life	vitamin, survive
equi–	prefix	same	equator, equilateral
semi–	prefix	half or part	semicircle, semicolon
–acy	suffix	quality	privacy, infancy
–age	suffix	activity	courage, shrinkage

Using Technology to Learn Word Parts

Several Web sites include lists of base words, prefixes, and suffixes. Reviewing these lists can help you build your vocabulary and prepare you to comprehend new words when you see them.

Spelling Changes from Suffixes

In most cases, adding a suffix does not change the spelling of a base word. However, if a base word ends in *e* and the suffix begins with a vowel, drop the *e*. Example: *struggle* plus *–ing* makes *struggling*.

Activity 3C Interpreting Word Parts

From each group of words, determine the meaning of the common word part. Use a dictionary for help.

1. accurate, acute, acupuncture

   acu- means _____

2. apolitical, atheist, apathy

   a– means _____

3. trickster, gangster, hipster

   –ster means _____

4. provoke, advocate, vocal

   vok- or *voc-* means _____

LESSON 4 HOW TO WRITE A RESEARCH REPORT

Following is a model showing the steps in writing a research report. Use these steps to help you write your own reports.

Step 1. Analyze the prompt.

The directions that explain what you are to research and write about are called the **prompt.** Pay close attention to what the prompt says.

- The prompt might be very broad. If it gives you many options, focus on a topic that is narrow enough that you can cover it well in the amount of time you have.

- The prompt might be very specific. If so, then follow it closely.

Write a thesis statement that will guide you as you write your essay in response to the prompt. For more on thesis statements, see page 28.

 Activity 4A *Analyzing the Prompt*

Read the following prompt. In the table that follows, indicate whether or not each report focus fits the prompt. Explain your answers.

> Write a two- to four-page report describing glaciers and their impact in shaping the landscape, climate, or other aspects of the physical world.

Report Focus	Does It Fit the Prompt?	Explanation
1. Origins of the term *glacier* and the use of *glacial* to mean slow		
2. Predictions on how the size of glaciers will change over the next century		
3. How glaciers influenced where lakes, rivers, and good farmland exist today		

Step 2. Take notes on sources.

Whether you need to find your own sources or they are provided for you on a test, take notes on them with your prompt in mind.

- Underline important facts or ideas in the source.

- Write notes in the margin about key ideas

- Write questions in the margin about anything that is unclear.

Following is an example of annotations you might make on a source.

> **Annotating Text**
>
> For more on how to annotate a text, see page 10.

©Perfection Learning® • No Reproduction Permitted.

Source 1

Storehouses of Freshwater

This excerpt provides an introduction to glaciers.

Even though you've probably never seen a glacier, they are a big item when we talk about the world's water supply. Almost 10 percent of the world's land mass is currently covered with glaciers, mostly in places like Greenland and Antarctica. Glaciers are important features in the hydrologic cycle and affect the volume, variability, and water quality of runoff in areas where they occur.

   In a way, glaciers are just frozen rivers of ice flowing downhill. Glaciers begin life as snowflakes. When the snowfall in an area far exceeds the melting that occurs during summer, glaciers start to form. The weight of the accumulated snow compresses the fallen snow into ice. These "rivers" of ice are tremendously heavy, and if they are on land that has a downhill slope the whole ice patch starts to slowly grind its way downhill. These glaciers can vary greatly in size, from a football-field sized patch to a river a hundred miles (161 kilometers) long.

Glaciers Affect the Landscape

   Glaciers have had a profound effect on the topography (lay of the land) in some areas, as in the northern U.S. You can imagine how a billion-ton ice cube can rearrange the landscape as it slowly grinds its way overland. . . . Many lakes, such as the Great Lakes, and valleys have been carved out by ancient glaciers. A massive icecap can be found in Greenland, where practically the whole country is covered with ice (shouldn't it be called Whiteland)? The ice on Greenland approaches two miles (3.2 kilometers) in thickness in some places and is so heavy that some of the land has been compressed so much that it is way below sea level.

Source: "Glaciers and Icecaps: Storehouses of Freshwater." United States Geological Service. Web. 23 March 2013. <usgs.gov>

Significance

Define hydrologic cycle?

Glaciers: frozen rivers

Check:
Wouldn't compressing snow make it warmer?

* Length: 100 miles

Define topography

* Weight: "billion-ton ice cube"
Formed Great Lakes, other lakes, valleys

* Thickness: 2 miles

©Perfection Learning® • No Reproduction Permitted.

T *Activity 4B Taking Notes*

Take notes on the following two excerpts. Annotate each source using notes, underlines, and symbols to help you understand the content and identify information for use in your essay in response to the prompt.

Source 2

Nature's Landscape Architect

The following excerpt is from an article that explains how glaciers shape the landscapes. It also defines some of the terms used in studying glaciers.

Glaciers are mighty sculptors of the landscape. They can carve wide valleys and deposit large expanses of rolling plains of sediment. How do they accomplish these feats? What are the various landforms that they can carry or deposit?

Arete: sharp, usually serrate, rock ridges between two steep, glacially sculpted slopes

Cirque: steep-walled, gentle floored, semicircular topographic hollow created by glacial excavation high in mountainous areas

Col: open, U-shaped pass across a high, narrow mountain rite created by glacial erosion

[The article defines other landforms created by glaciers, including fjords, truncated spurs, and whalebacks.]

Glacial Basins: One thing that glaciers do well, given favorable conditions such as thick, fast-moving, warm ice and well-jointed bedrock, is excavation. Localized excavation can create closed bedrock basins, many of which ultimately harbor lakes. Examples of these lakes are tarns and paternoster lakes. Tarns are single lakes. Paternoster lakes are a string of lakes connected by a trunk stream.

Source: "Nature's Landscape Architects." National Park Service. Web. 23 March 2013. <nature.nps.gov>.

    ©Perfection Learning® • No Reproduction Permitted.

Source 3

Glaciers' Gifts by William Cronon

This excerpt is from an environmental history of Chicago.

[Glaciers] altered everything in their path. Far to the north, on the ancient rocks that would become northern Minnesota, Wisconsin, and Michigan, the ice stripped the land of its soil leaving it badly drained and not very fertile. Grinding southward, the glaciers gouged out tiny ponds and enormous lakes, finally depositing immense loads of soil and gravel wherever they paused in their advances and retreat. Illinois and Iowa, southern Wisconsin and Minnesota, and Chicago itself were all blessed with these Ice Age gifts from the north. . . . Then, as the glaciers disappeared, enormous volumes of water released from their melting ice carved new routes for the major watercourses of the region, creating or reshaping rivers as different as the Chicago, the Wisconsin, and the Mississippi.

Source: Cronon, William. *Nature's Metropolis.* New York: Norton, 1991. Page 35. Print.

Step 3. Organize your ideas.

Determine the best order in which to present your ideas. The order should be logical so that readers can follow your ideas easily. Making an outline before you write the first draft of your report will help you organize your ideas. A research report consists of three basic parts:

- The **introduction** should state the topic clearly, usually in one paragraph.
- The **body** should present the research. Each main point should have its own paragraph.
- The **conclusion** should restate the topic and summarize the research in the last paragraph.

Following is a sample outline for a research report about glaciers.

Sample Outline: The Impact of Glaciers

I. **Introduction**
    A. Glaciers have been important for thousands of years.
    B. Glaciers have influenced where lakes, rivers, and good farmland exist today.

II. **Body**
    A. Glaciers can be enormous.
        1. The size of a glacier can be described in various ways.
            a. Some glaciers are like a river, a hundred miles long.
            b. A glacier can be like "a billion-ton ice cube."
            c. In Greenland, the ice is almost two miles thick.
        2. Glaciers cover about ten percent of the world's land.
    B. Glaciers in the past shaped the world of today.
        1. As glaciers slide downhill, they scrape off the soil
        2. Glaciers carved valleys and lakes.
            a. They formed the Great Lakes.
            b. They formed single lakes called tarns.
            c. They formed strings of lakes, called paternoster lakes.
    C. The Midwest was shaped by glaciers.
        1. Glaciers scraped dirt off land in the north.
        2. Glaciers deposited the dirt in Illinois and Iowa.
        3. Water from glaciers formed rivers and lakes.

III. **Conclusion**
    A. The development of the Midwest and other regions was shaped 13,000 years ago by the glaciers.
    B. Glaciers from long ago shape the world today.

Step 4. Write the draft.

Below is a first draft of the report on glaciers. It is based on the outline and the sources. It includes mistakes that you will fix in later activities.

 ©Perfection Learning® • No Reproduction Permitted.

Sample Draft: The Impact of Glaciers

Imagine a river of ice, moving slowly down stream as more snow and ice are added to it each year. This a glacier. Glaciers cover about one-tenth of the land surface of the earth. They have influenced where lakes, rivers, and good farmland exist today.

Glaciers come in all sizes. Some are small. Some are enormous. A glacier is "a billion-ton ice cube." Some glaciers are like rivers. However, they are frozen. They stretch for up to one hundred miles. Glaciers in Greenland are nearly two miles thick.

Something as big as a glacier has big effects. As snow is added to a glacier, it gets larger. If a glacier is on land that slopes at all, the glacier will slowly slide downhill. As it does, it scrapes off the soil. Glaciers are so large and heavy that they can carve out deep valleys. If these valleys fill with water they form lakes. Single lakes are called *tarns*. Strings of lakes are called *paternoster lakes.* Some of the most impressive lakes caused by glaciers are the Great Lakes.

The Midwest is an excellent example of the power of glaciers to shape the landscape. As glacier grew, they scraped the dirt off of land in northern Minnesota and Wisconsin and pushed it or carried it south. As they moved south, they gouged out thousands of small lakes throughout Minnesota. Glaciers also created the Great Lakes of Superior, Michigan, Huron, Erie, and Ontario. When the climate started to warm and the glaciers began to recede, or retreat. As they did, they deposited their dirt in Illinois and Iowa. The water from the melting glaciers formed the rivers of the Midwest, including the Mississippi.

The economy of the Midwest today shows how important glaciers of the past were. Northern Minnesota and Wisconsin do not have great farmland, but they have wonderful lakes that attract tourists. Iowa and Illinois have the best farmland in the world, and the grow amazing amounts of corn and soybeans every year. Glaciers are not only enormous, but they have been enormously important.

Step 5. Revise your essay.

After you write a draft, revise it to make it clearer and more precise. Avoid unnecessary repetition. For example, compare these two sentences from the sample:

- "Some of the most impressive lakes caused by glaciers are the Great Lakes."
- "Glaciers also created the Great Lakes of Superior, Michigan, Huron, Erie, and Ontario."

These two sentences are so similar that one of them could be deleted.

In addition, if you use the same sentence pattern over and over, change some of them. The chart below lists four types of sentences.

Type of Sentence	Elements	Example
Simple	one subject and one verb	Some glaciers are enormous.
Compound	two or more simple sentences connected by a comma and a coordinating conjunction, such as *and, or, but,* or *yet*	Some glaciers are enormous, but many are small.
Complex	one independent clause and one or more subordinate clauses	Some glaciers are enormous, which explains their importance.
Compound-complex	two or more independent clauses and one or more dependent clauses	Some glaciers are enormous, and some are small, according to scientists.

Activity 4C Revising for Sentence Variety

The second paragraph of the sample draft consists only of simple sentences. Rewrite the paragraph using at least one compound sentence, one complex sentence, and one compound-complex sentence.

Glaciers come in all sizes. Some are small. Some are enormous. A glacier is "a billion-ton ice cube." Some glaciers are like rivers. However, they are frozen. They stretch for up to one hundred miles. Glaciers in Greenland are nearly two miles thick.

_____

_____

_____

_____

_____

_____

  ©Perfection Learning® • No Reproduction Permitted.

Acquiring New Words

As you research, you will probably see words that are new to you. For example, the second source, "Nature's Landscape Architect," uses several words that you might not know.

- Words such as *sediment, excavation, bedrock, tarn, paternoster,* and *trunk stream* are **domain-specific words,** words that are commonly used in a specific academic area, such as geography.

- Words such as *sculptors, localized,* and *ultimately* are common in discussions about many topics.

To find the pronunciation of a word, to determine or clarify its precise meaning, or to identify its part of speech, consult a dictionary, glossary, thesaurus, or other reference material. Here is an example of a dictionary entry for the word *sediment*:

> **sed•i•ment** (seh'-dah-mehnt) *noun* **1.** solid material that settles to the bottom of a liquid **2.** solid material that is transported and then left behind by the movement of air, water, or ice

The above entry includes these elements:

- the entry word is in bold and divided into syllables
- the pronunciation is in parentheses, using a system of symbols that are explained somewhere in the dictionary, often near the front
- the part of speech is in italics
- two definitions for the entry word

Dictionaries often include additional information about the origin of the word, advice on its usage, examples of synonyms, and related forms of the word such as plurals or other tenses.

Activity 4D Using Reference Materials

Use a print dictionary, an online dictionary, or another source to answer each question about a word found in "Nature's Landscape Architect."

1. How many syllables are in the geography term *arete*? _____

2. Does *cirque* mostly nearly rhyme with *due, hay,* or *lurk*? _____

3. What part of speech is *col*? _____

4. What is a *fjord*? _____

_____

Step 6. Edit and proofread your essay.

After revising your report, proofread it for mistakes in spelling, punctuation, and grammar.

©Perfection Learning® • No Reproduction Permitted.

Reference Materials

Reference materials are not intended to be read from the first page to the last. The writers of reference materials assume that readers want to answer specific questions, such as: When was the last ice age? How should I pronounce *paternoster?* Ask librarians or teachers to help you find print and digital reference materials to help you in your research.

Technology and Pronunciation

Many online dictionary sites include sound so you can listen to pronunciations.

LESSON 5 YOU TRY IT

Now it is your turn to write a research report. Use the steps outlined in this chapter to guide you as you write.

Step 1. Analyze the prompt.

Step 2. Take notes on sources.

Step 3. Organize your ideas.

Step 4. Write the draft.

Step 5. Revise your essay.

Step 6. Edit and proofread your essay.

Sharing Your Research

Research reports are often the longest and most in-depth writing assignment that you will do in school. You may wish to share your work with your classmates, your parents, or other individuals. Use e-mail, a social network site, or another form of technology to transmit your finished report.

 Activity 5A Writing a Research Report

Write a research report in response to one of the following prompts.

A. Profiling an Artist	B. Video Violence
Painters, musicians, and other artists have all shaped history. Write a research report on one influential artist from world history. Your report should be two to four pages long. Use at least three sources in your report and cite your sources in the text.	Does watching a violent video game or movie make a person more likely to commit an act of violence? Write a research report on the impact of violence in popular entertainment. Your report should be two to four pages long. Use at least three sources in your report and cite your sources in the text.

My writing has . . .	
DEVELOPMENT	❏ a clear question to answer or problem to solve ❏ a topic appropriate to the length of the report
ORGANIZATION	❏ a clear introduction, body, and conclusion ❏ good transitions to maintain the flow of ideas ❏ logical order
EVIDENCE	❏ strong, relevant textual evidence ❏ information from multiple authoritative sources
LANGUAGE & STYLE	❏ precise, appropriate word choice ❏ a formal, objective tone
GRAMMAR, SPELLING, & PUNCTUATION	❏ standard grammar ❏ correct spelling ❏ proper punctuation

©Perfection Learning® • No Reproduction Permitted.

Writing a Literary Analysis

A literary analysis interprets elements of one or more poems, short stories, or other works of literature. It supports that interpretation with appropriate evidence from the text, such as quotations and other details. In addition, a literary analysis may includes facts and informed judgments from other sources, such as biographies of the writer or historical works about the events described in the literature.

LESSON 1 ELEMENTS OF A LITERARY ANALYSIS

A literary analysis essay requires you to look at specific elements of a work of literature. Below are some commonly used literary devices found in stories and poems and how you might write about them.

Definitions of Literary Elements	A prompt may ask you to analyze how . . .
Characterization: description of the characters in the story	• characters develop and change • characters advance the plot • characters develop the theme
Plot: events in the story	• events in the story influence the characters • the author uses events to create mystery or tension
Structure: the arrangement of lines of poetry or the order in which ideas are presented	• the structure supports the theme
Setting: where and when the events take place	• the setting influences the plot and the characters' choices
Tone: author's attitude toward the writing	• the author's choice of words creates the tone
Point of View: who is narrating the events	• point of view influences the story or poem
Theme: central idea of a text	• the theme is developed, shaped, and refined by specific details • two passages on the same topic or with the same theme are similar or different
Figurative Language: words that express additional meaning beyond their literal meaning	• imagery or sound devices convey meaning • the author uses similes and metaphors about nature throughout the text

Collaboration on Figurative Language

In a small group, develop three examples of each type of figurative language described below.

- **Imagery** is the use of vivid details that appeal to the senses. Example: The just-baked apple pie gave the tiny kitchen the sweet aroma of welcome.

- **Personification** is the use of human qualities to describe something that is not human. Example: The apple pie, knowing the grandchildren had arrived, shouted, "Welcome!"

- A **simile** is a comparison using the words *like* or *as*. Example: Life is like baseball.

- A **metaphor** is a comparison that does not use *like* or *as*. Example: Grandpa was in the ninth inning of life.

©Perfection Learning® • No Reproduction Permitted.

Activity 1A Understanding Literary Devices

Choose a work of literature you have read recently. Complete the following tasks to help you analyze the work.

Title: _____

1. Analyze the main characters:

_____

_____

_____

2. Summarize the plot:

_____

_____

_____

3. Describe the setting:

_____

_____

_____

4. Identify the tone:

_____

_____

5. Analyze the point of view:

_____

_____

_____

6. Explain the theme:

_____

_____

_____

7. Interpret two examples of figurative language:

_____

_____

Technology and Figurative Language

One way to think of creative figurative language is to do an Internet search for images, using an adverb or adjective as the search term. Searching for a common term, such as *happy* or *quickly* will bring up images that you may not have expected.

LESSON 2 EVIDENCE FROM TEXTS

Literary analysis is based on reading a text closely in order to gather evidence about the characters and theme. On a test, you may be asked to analyze a poem, a short story, or an excerpt from a literary work and then write an essay about it.

The following paragraph is from Nathaniel Hawthorne's short story, "Young Goodman Brown." In it, Brown meets a man in the forest and the two walk deeper into the woods together. The details provide clues about the significance of the other man.

> As they went, he [the other man] plucked a branch of maple to serve for a walking stick, and began to strip it of the twigs and little boughs [branches], which were wet with evening dew. The moment his fingers touched them they became strangely withered and dried up as with a week's sunshine.

- The "twigs and little boughs, which were wet" suggests the branch was full of life when the man plucked it.

- However, one touch from the man and the boughs "became strangely withered and dried up." The man's touch seems to cause death.

From this passage, a reader can infer that the man represents something bad. As the story progresses, the reader realizes that the man symbolizes evil, and the story's plot is about Brown's reaction to it.

> **Point of View in Literature**
>
> When taking notes on a short story, novel, or poem, always identify which character you are commenting on. Each character may have a distinctive point of view. Usually, one of them speaks for the author.

Using Context

When you come across words that are new to you, you can often figure out their meaning from the context. The **context** includes the other words and the topic of the passage. For example, what is the meaning of *forfeit* in this passage?

> By game time, so many players had the flu that we did not have enough people to play. We had to *forfeit*. We were disappointed to lose to our rivals that way.

The context indicates that the speaker's team did not have enough players to compete, so it lost without playing. *Forfeit* means to lose or give up something for breaking the rules.

Activity 2A Understanding Words and Key Ideas

The following excerpt is from "Baker's Bluejay Yarn" by Mark Twain. It is a humorous tale about a man who convinces others that he can understand animals. Here he is talking about how bluejays talk.

> There's more to a bluejay than any other creature. . . there's no bird, or cow, or anything that uses as good grammar as a bluejay. You may say a cat uses good grammar. Well, a cat does—but you let a cat get excited once; you let a cat get to pulling fur with another cat on a shed, nights, and you'll hear grammar that will give you the lockjaw. Ignorant people think it's the noise which fighting cats make that is so aggravating, but it ain't so; it's the sickening grammar they use. Now I've never heard a jay use bad grammar but very seldom.

Part A
Circle the letter before the choice that best explains what "pulling fur" means as used in the excerpt.

a. battling

c. resting

b. grooming

d. talking

Part B

Circle the letter before the two choices that most help a reader understand the meaning of "pulling fur."

a. "a cat uses good grammar"

b. "let a cat get excited"

c. "the noise which fighting cats make"

d. "but very seldom"

You can often figure out the meaning of a word or phrase from its context. You can verify your determination of the meaning of the word or phrase by looking it up in a print or an online dictionary. The dictionary can also provide additional information about the word or phrase:

- its precise meaning, so you use it as readers expect you to

- its pronunciation, so you can say it in a way listeners will understand

- its part of speech, so you can use it correctly

Often books include a **glossary,** which is a dictionary of important terms used in that book.

 ## Activity 2B Identifying the Key Idea

Answer the following questions about the key idea in "Baker's Bluejay Yarn."

Part A

Circle the letter before the choice that best summarizes the key idea in this paragraph.

a. bluejays are the smartest of all animals

b. birds, cows, and other animals make mistakes in grammar

c. many people think cats use good grammar

d. ignorant people don't like the noise made by animals

Part B

Circle the letter before the two choices that provides textual evidence to support your answer in Part A.

a. "more to a bluejay than any other creature"

b. "grammar that will give you the lockjaw"

c. "You may say a cat uses good grammar"

d. "the noise which fighting cats make that is so aggravating"

e. "I've never heard a jay use bad grammar but very seldom"

> **Sources on a Test**
>
> Writing tests might include one or more sources that provide the evidence you need to write an essay. These sources might be literary or informational. As you read them, think about the main idea and key details in each one.

Figures of Speech: Allusions

To gather information from your sources, you will need to interpret the figures of speech in them. One common type of figure of speech is an **allusion,** which is an indirect reference to something the writer assumes the reader already knows. Below are examples of three common types of allusions.

Type	Example	Reference	Meaning
Literature	Every four years, June is the cruelest month for sprinters trying out for the Olympic team.	In the first line of his famous poem *The Waste Land,* T. S. Eliot states that "April is the cruelest month," maybe because it gives people a false sense of hope.	Sprinters who fail to make the Olympic team are disappointed.
Mythology	By modifying the mouse's genes, the biologist created a little Hercules.	In Greek and Roman mythology, Hercules was a hero known for his strength.	The mouse was very strong.
Bible	Mr. Patel, nicknamed "Job" by his principal, was a great teacher.	In a Biblical story, Job shows great patience as he suffers from a series of misfortunes designed to test his faith in God.	Mr. Patel was very patient with students.

As a writer, you can use allusions most effectively when you are confident that your readers have the knowledge to understand your comment. With a well-chosen allusion, you can communicate a tremendous amount of information to your reader with only a few words. For example, if your readers know the story of Cinderella, describing an object as "like a glass slipper" may tell your readers in four words what you would need four sentences to explain.

Activity 2C Using Allusions

Write a sentence using each type of allusion. Your audience is your class. To help you think of ideas, look up possible topics in reference works.

1. Literature

_____

_____

_____

2   Mythology

_____

_____

_____

> ### Collaborating on Allusions
>
> Discuss the allusions you write for Activity 2C with a classmate. See if each of you has the right knowledge to understand the allusion.

©Perfection Learning® • No Reproduction Permitted.

LESSON 3 HOW TO WRITE A LITERARY ANALYSIS

A literary analysis may ask you to focus on specific elements of the text, such as the theme, the characters, the point of view, or the word choice. Whatever element you focus on, supply textual evidence to support your analysis. The following will help you break down the process of writing a literary analysis into manageable steps.

Step 1. Analyze the prompt.

The directions for writing a literary analysis are called the **prompt.** For example, here is a prompt:

> Wealth, poverty, happiness, and greed were common themes in the writing of Leo Tolstoy, the great Russian writer of the 1800s. Write a literary analysis of Tolstoy's story "How Much Land Does a Man Need?" Focus on how greed provides a motive for the thoughts and actions of characters. Cite textual evidence from the story to support your analysis.

Activity 3A Interpreting a Prompt

Summarize the above prompt in your own words, using up to 30 words.

_____

_____

_____

Step 2. Take notes on the text.

To increase your understanding and appreciation of a text, read it more than once. You will gain a deeper understanding of it each time you reread it. As you read, make notes about the text. Some of your notes might focus on these topics:

- Write questions about why characters say or do things.

- Ask why the writer mentions specific details.

- Comment on any surprising changes of direction in the plot.

- Highlight any figurative language.

For more on annotating sources, see page 10.

Activity 3B Annotating a Story

With the prompt from Step 1 in mind, annotate the following story.

Source 1

How Much Land Does a Man Need? by Leo Tolstoy

Leo Tolstoy was born in Russia in 1828 and lived until 1910. His commitment to peace and justice inspired both Mahatma Gandhi and Martin Luther King Jr. The following source is an excerpt adapted from one of his short stories.

The ambitious peasant Pakhom, who, after gaining ever greater plots of land, finally heard of a wonderful deal in a far-off country. He travelled to the land of the Bashkirs and negotiated with the village elder, who seemed a fool. The elder told Pakhom that he could have all the land he wanted for a thousand rubles a day.

Pakhom did not understand. "What kind of rate is that—a day?" he asked. "How many acres could that be?"

"We don't reckon your way. We sell by the day. However much you can walk around in one day will be yours."

When Pakhom expressed that a man can walk around much land in one day, the elder burst out laughing. "And all of it will be yours!" he replied. But there was one condition: If Pakhom didn't return to the starting point by sundown, the money would be forfeited.

Ecstatic, Pakhom spent a sleepless night. Rising at dawn, he went with the villagers to the top of a hill where the elder put down his hat. After placing his thousand rubles on top, Pakhom began walking, digging holes along the way to mark his land. The going was easy and he thought, "I'll do another three miles and then turn left. The land's so beautiful here, it would be a pity to miss any."

Pakhom hurried throughout the morning, going out of his way to add more land. But at noon when he looked back at the hill where he had begun, it was difficult to see the people. Maybe I have gone too far, he worried, and decided he must begin to make shorter sides. As the afternoon wore on, the heat was exhausting. By now

---

       ©Perfection Learning® • No Reproduction Permitted.

his bare feet were cut and bruised, and his legs weakened. He wanted to rest, but it was out of the question.

Pakhom struggled on, walking faster, then running. He worried that he had been too greedy and his fear made him breathless. On he ran, his shirt soaked and his throat parched. His lungs were working like a blacksmith's bellows, his heart beat like a hammer. He was terrified.

All this strain will be the death of me [said Pakhom to himself]. Although Pakhom feared death, he couldn't stop. They'd call me an idiot, he thought. When he was close enough to hear the Bashkirs cheering, he summoned his last ounce of strength and kept running. As he finally reached the hill, everything suddenly became dark—the sun had set. Pakhom groaned. He wanted to stop, but heard the Bashkirs still cheering him on. He realized that from where he was at the bottom of the hill, the sun had set—but not for those on top. Pakhom took a deep breath and rushed up the hill. Reaching the top, he saw the elder sitting by the hat, laughing his head off. Pakhom's legs gave way, and he fell forward grasping the cap.

"Oh, well done," exclaimed the elder.

"That's a lot of land you've earned yourself!"

Pakhom's worker ran up and tried to lift his master, but Pakhom was dead. The worker picked up Pakhom's spade, dug a grave, and buried him—six feet from head to heel, exactly the amount of land a man needs.

Step 3. Write a thesis statement.

After you've gathered notes, write a thesis statement to guide your writing. The **thesis statement** should clearly state the central idea of your literary analysis. It should fit both the prompt and your notes.

Step 4. Organize your ideas.

Think about how you will organize your notes and your thesis statement into a cohesive essay. Consider what you will say in your introduction, body, and conclusion. Before writing your essay, develop an outline to organize the main ideas and supporting details.

Activity 3C Writing a Thesis Statement and Outline

Complete the following outline by filling in the blanks.

Sample Outline: The Danger of Greed

Thesis Statement: **Greed causes** _____

_____

I.   **Introduction**

   A. Leo Tolstoy is _____

   B. Greed causes people to do terrible things to
      themselves and to others.

II. **Body: How Much Land Does a Man Need?**

   A. The plot is simple.

      1. The Bashkirs will give Pakhom all the land he
         can walk around in one day in exchange for

         _____

      2. Pakhom tries to walk around so much land
         that he dies from exhaustion and is buried.

   B. Pakhom is greedy.

      1. In the first line, he is described as an _____

         _____

      2. He "spent a sleepless night" before his walk.

      3. Though exhausted, he fears being called an idiot

         more _____

   C. The village elder is happy.

      1. At the beginning of the story, he laughs when __

         _____

      2. At the end of the story, he laughs when _____

         _____

III. **Conclusion**

   A. The story criticizes greed.

      1. Greed drives the characters and the plot.

      2. One person died from greed and one_____

         _____

   B. Greed is still a problem today.

Technology and Outlines

Many word processing programs include autoformatting options that will style an outline for you. This option will create indents and use different type styles for each level of information. You can also format your outline manually.

Citations

In some writing assignments, you will need to identify your sources in your text. For examples showing how to do this, see page 46. In literary analysis, all of the citations may come from one text. If so, only the page number is needed. If the work is short, such as a one-page poem, no citation may be needed at all.

Step 5. Write the draft.

Following is a draft of a literary analysis. It includes passages and misspelled words that you will revise or edit in later activities.

Sample Draft: Greed in a Tolstoy Story

Leo Tolstoy was a famous Russian writer who lived from 1828 to 1910. He loved the Russian people and believed strongly in the teachings of Jesus about justice. In his short story "How Much Land Does a Man Need?," Tolstoy shows how greed makes people do terrible things to themselves and to each other.

The plot of the story is simple. For a fee of 1,000 rubles, the Bashkirs will sell a person all the land that person can walk around in one day. A man named Pakhom takes up the offer. However, he tries to walk around so much land that he deis from the effort. In the end, all the land a man needs is a tiney plot in which to be buried.

The main character of the story, Pakhom is greedy. In the very first sentence, Tolsty describes him as an "ambitious peasant." Pakhom is so excited by the chance to sieze land for feilds that he "spent a sleepless night" before the event. As the day of walking goes on, he grows more and more tired. By the end of the day, he is very tired. However, he fears being called an ideot more than he fears death. So he pushed onward until he succeeds. The effort kills him.

The other important character in the story is the village elder of the Bashkirs. He is a very happy man. At the beginning of the story, he "burst out laughing" when he makes the deal with Pakhom. At the end, as he sees Pakhom finish successfully and collapsing in death, he is "laughing his head off." The elder understands that he will benefit form Pakhom's greed.

Tolstoy's story is a powerful attack on greed. Pakhom pays for his greed with his life. While Pakhom suffers, the village elder goes on. However, the village elder represents those who are so greedy that they use the greed of others for their own gain. Tolstoy's lesson seems clear: not only will a greedy person suffer, but greed will make people so terible that they benefit from the suffering of others.

Step 6. Revise your analysis.

After writing a draft, revise it to make the ideas clearer and more specific. You can do this using synonyms, antonyms, and analogies.

Analogies, Similes, and Metaphors

Analogies, similes, and metaphors are all types of comparisons. Analogies are more complex than the other two because they compare the relationship between one pair of things with the relationship between another pair of things.

- A **synonym** is a word that has nearly the same meaning as another word. *Greed, craving,* and *avarice* are synonyms. All describe a strong desire, although each has its own nuance. As you revise, replace words with synonyms that express your thoughts more precisely.

- An **antonym** is a word that means the opposite of another word. *Greed* and *generosity* are antonyms. As you revise, consider whether you can use an antonym to highlight a contrast. Example: She is greedy but her sister is generous.

- An **analogy** is a logical relationship between a pair of words. As you revise, consider analogies to add depth to your writing. Instead of writing "Benito Juárez was an important and beloved president of Mexico," use an analogy such as "Benito Juárez was to Mexico what Abraham Lincoln was to the United States."

Activity 3D Identifying Synonyms and Antonyms

Add a synonym and antonym for each word. Use a dictionary if needed.

Word	Synonym	Antonym
early	1.	2.
great	3.	4.
fast	5.	6.
smart	7.	8.
rich	9.	10.

Activity 3E Completing Analogies

Fill in the missing words to complete the analogies.

1. president is to country as governor is to _____

2. basketball is to sport as _____ is to mathematics

3. flexible is to _____ as modern is to old-fashioned

4. _____ is to courage as cunning is to slyness

Activity 3F Revising with Precise Language

Rewrite each sentence replacing the words in italics with more precise words or an analogy. Make additional changes as needed in the sentence.

1. By the end of the day, he is very *tired.*

   _____

   _____

2. While Pakhom *suffers,* the village elder *goes on.*

   _____

   _____

3. A *man* named Pakhom takes up the offer.

   _____

   _____

Step 7. Edit and proofread your analysis.

After you revise your draft, read it again. Correct any errors in grammar, punctuation, and spelling.

Activity 3G Editing the Sample Essay

Reread the sample essay. Circle any misspelled words and write the correctly spelled word in the margin. Several words that include ie *or* ei *are misspelled.*

> **Spelling Words with *ie* or *ei***
> ....
>
> In words with *ie* or *ei*, the *i* usually comes before the *e*, as in *believe* and *thief.* Common exceptions include:
>
> - If the letters follow *c*, the *e* usually comes before the *i*, as in *receive.*
> - If the letters stand for a long *a* sound, the *e* usually comes before the *i*, as in *eight* and *veil.*
>
> Exceptions to these patterns include *height, neither,* and *ancient.*

LESSON 4 YOU TRY IT

Now it is your turn to write a literary analysis. Use the steps outlined in this chapter.

 Activity 4A Writing a Literary Analysis

Choose one of the following prompts and write a literary analysis using the steps outlined in this chapter. Then use the checklist to make sure your writing conforms to the Characteristics of Good Writing.

A. Analyzing a Literary Character	B. Analyzing Figurative Language
Writers develop characters by describing what the characters think, say, and do. Write an analysis of a one of your favorite literary characters. Use quotations from the work in your analysis. Your analysis should be between two and four pages long.	Find an example online of a story written by a student. Write an analysis of the figurative language used in it. Use quotations from the story in your analysis. Your analysis should be between two and four pages long.

Use the following checklist to edit your essay.

Steps for Writing a Literary Analysis

1. Analyze the prompt.
2. Take notes on the text.
3. Write a thesis statement.
4. Organize your ideas.
5. Write the draft.
6. Revise your analysis.
7. Edit and proofread your analysis.

	My writing has . . .
DEVELOPMENT	❐ a clear thesis statement ❐ strong supporting points ❐ addressed all the requirements of the prompt
ORGANIZATION	❐ a clear introduction, body, and conclusion ❐ good transitions ❐ logical order
EVIDENCE	❐ strong, relevant textual evidence ❐ direct quotations or paraphrased information from other texts
LANGUAGE & STYLE	❐ precise, appropriate word choice ❐ a formal, objective tone
GRAMMAR, SPELLING, & PUNCTUATION	❐ standard grammar ❐ correct spelling ❐ proper punctuation

©Perfection Learning® • No Reproduction Permitted.

Writing a Narrative

A **narrative** is a text that tells a story. The story, whether real or imagined, is always based on a problem, a situation, or an observation.

LESSON 1 ENGAGING THE READER

The beginning of a narrative needs to establish the story's context and narrator. **Context** includes the time and place of the story, and the basic reason for the events in it. The reader needs to know the setting in order to interpret the events correctly. The **narrator** is the voice who tells the story.

- In a **first-person narrative,** the narrator tells the story from his or her point of view. For example: "I saw my friend Billy board the airplane." Use first-person to make your story feel very personal.

- In a **third-person narrative,** the narrator tells the story without being part of it. For example: "Joe saw his friend Billy board the airplane." Use third-person to make your story feel more objective.

> **Pronoun Clues to the Point of View**
>
> You can tell the difference between a first-person and a third-person narrative by the pronouns they use.
>
> - A first-person narrator uses *I, me, my, we, us,* and *our.*
>
> - A third-person narrator uses *he, she, him, her, his, hers, they, them,* and *their.*

Activity 1A Evaluating the Context

Below is the first paragraph from "The Jilting of Granny Weatherall" by Katherine Anne Porter. It was first published in 1929. Read it and answer the questions about the context it sets for the rest of the story.

> She flicked her wrist neatly out of Doctor Harry's pudgy careful fingers and pulled the sheet up to her chin. The brat ought to be in knee breeches. Doctoring around the country with spectacles on his nose! "Get along now, take your schoolbooks and go. There's nothing wrong with me."

1. Where is the woman and what is her situation?

_____

2. Explain whether the first sentence is in first-person or third-person.

_____

3. Explain the meaning of "There's nothing wrong with me."

_____

_____

4. Describe the female character as she is introduced here.

_____

_____

LESSON 2 NARRATIVE TECHNIQUES

When you write a narrative, you can use several techniques to help you describe experiences, to explain why events happened, and to portray characters. Three common techniques are listed below.

- **Dialogue** consists of words spoken by characters in the story. These words are enclosed in quotation marks. Dialogue helps characters come alive for readers.

- **Pacing** is the speed at which events happen. By varying the pacing, writers keep readers engaged in the story.

- **Description** includes specific details about people, things, and events. These details help the reader imagine what the writer is portraying.

 ## Activity 2A Identifying Narrative Techniques

The following excerpt is from A Light in the Sky *by Cynthia Mercati. The story is set in France during World War II (1939–1945). The British and the French are fighting against the Germans, known as Nazis. The Nazis have just shot down a British plane over France. The narrator, a French girl, hopes to rescue the pilot before the Nazis capture him.*

1. Underline two examples of dialogue.

2. Place parentheses around three examples of description that provide specific details about people, things, or events.

> "Please," I whispered as I ran, "please don't let the Nazis get there first!"
>
> Then just a few feet away, I saw the clearing. I was right! This was exactly where the pilot had bailed out! His parachute was caught on the branches of a tree.
>
> I have to get that down, I thought. The whiteness of it is like a light, leading the Nazis right to this spot. Suddenly I froze in my tracks. I covered my eyes with both hands. A pencil-thin light was shining directly into my eyes. I heard a gun being cocked. My stomach turned over in fear.
>
> Then I heard a surprised gasp. "You're just a kid!"

Narrative Techniques in Other Types of Writing

The techniques used in narrative writing are also used in other types of writing. Bring to class examples of each technique described in this chapter. Share them with a small group and decide which type of writing each example represents.

   ©Perfection Learning® • No Reproduction Permitted.

LESSON 3 SEQUENCE OF EVENTS

As the writer, you decide the order in which to present events in a narrative. You can present the events in three different sequences.

- Start at the beginning and present the events in the order they happened. This type of organization is called **chronological order**. This order is easy for readers to follow.

- Start in the middle. If you choose a dramatic moment, you can grab the attention of readers. Then you can fill in the earlier events to explain the moment before you tell the rest of the story.

- Start at the end. You give away the ending, but you can focus on the process that led up to the result.

To present the sequence of events smoothly, use transition words such as those in the chart below.

Connection	Words and Phrases to Make Connections			
Addition	in addition	furthermore	moreover	as well
Example	for example	for instance	specifically	namely
Comparison	similarly	in the same way	likewise	coincidentally
Contrast	however	nevertheless	in contrast	on the other hand
Chronology	before	meanwhile	at the same time	prior
	next	then	later	soon
Result	thus	therefore	as a result	consequently
Summary	finally	in conclusion	hence	to summarize

 ### Activity 3A Identifying Transition Words

Underline four transition words in this paragraph.

> The offer was tempting. I wanted to go to a movie. Specifically, I wanted to see *Car Wars*. In addition, I wanted to see my friends. I had not seen them in two weeks. However, I had homework to finish. It wasn't going to do itself. Finally, I decided to stay home. The movie would have to wait.

 ### Activity 3B Writing with Transition Words

Write a passage that uses two transition words. Underline them.

_____

_____

_____

LESSON 4 DESCRIPTIVE LANGUAGE

When you write, choose precise words, specific details, and sensory words to capture the action and convey experiences and events. **Sensory words** are ones that appeal to the five senses: sight, hearing, taste, smell, and touch. The table gives you some examples of weak and strong descriptive language.

Category	Weak Description	Strong Description
Precise Words	I was tired.	I felt drained of energy, like a runner after completing a marathon.
Specific Details	The man looked odd.	The man's bright orange shirt, lime-green tie, and cheerful smile made him stand out at the funeral.
Sensory Words	The room made me uncomfortable.	As I entered the room, the glaring light and the stench of unwashed gym clothes assaulted my eyes and nose.

Activity 4A Using Precise Words and Phrases

Rewrite the following paragraph using more precise words and phrases.

My new school was large. The original building had been added onto many times. The hallways were hard to follow. I could not find my way around easily at first.

Technology and Precise Language

If you are trying to use precise words that you do not usually use, you may want help in knowing how to use them correctly. Search for the word on the Internet. You will get definitions from several dictionaries. In addition, you will get the word used in various contexts.

_____

_____

_____

_____

_____

_____

_____

_____

©Perfection Learning® • No Reproduction Permitted.

LESSON 5 CONCLUSION

Like other types of writing, a narrative ends with a conclusion. A strong conclusion should make the reader feel the story is complete. It should

- follow from the rest of the narrative

- wrap up any loose ends

Sometimes, the conclusion includes reflections on the story or puts the story into a broader context. In some narratives, the conclusion is a surprise ending.

The length of the conclusion depends on the length of the narrative. If the text is only a page or two long, the conclusion might be only a sentence. In a full-length novel, the entire last chapter might be the conclusion.

Activity 5A Writing a Conclusion

Imagine that you have a classmate, Hector, who enters a spelling competition. He dedicates himself to winning the national title. Hector spends so much time studying for it that he drops out of his other activities, fails to do his homework, and ignores his friends. He wins the local title and the state title, and then he finishes fourth in the national competition. Write a conclusion to a story about Hector's efforts and the results. Describe Hector's feelings about his experience and the lessons that he learned.

_____

_____

_____

_____

_____

_____

_____

_____

_____

_____

_____

_____

LESSON 6 HOW TO WRITE A NARRATIVE

Following is a model demonstrating the five steps in writing a narrative. Use these steps to help you as you write.

Step 1. Analyze the prompt.

The directions for writing a narrative essay are called the **prompt**. Follow the prompt closely. Here is a sample of a prompt:

> "How Much Land Does a Man Need?" is told by a narrator who is not in the story. Rewrite the tale from the perspective of a character in it: Pakhom, the village elder, or Pakhom's worker. Add details from your imagination to fill in the story.

Step 2. Take notes on sources.

Annotate the source, noting items that will help you address the prompt.

Activity 6A Analyzing the Prompt and the Source

Analyze the prompt in Step 1 and the source below to prepare you to write a response to the prompt.

Source 1

How Much Land Does a Man Need? by Leo Tolstoy

The ambitious peasant Pakhom, who, after gaining ever greater plots of land, finally heard of a wonderful deal in a far-off country. He travelled to the land of the Bashkirs and negotiated with the village elder, who seemed a fool. The elder told Pakhom that he could have all the land he wanted for a thousand rubles a day.

Pakhom did not understand. "What kind of rate is that—a day?" he asked. "How many acres could that be?"

"We don't reckon your way. We sell by the day. However much you can walk around in one day will be yours."

When Pakhom expressed that a man can walk around much land in one day, the elder burst out laughing. "And all of it will be yours!" he replied. But there was one condition: If Pakhom didn't return to the starting point by sundown, the money would be forfeited.

Ecstatic, Pakhom spent a sleepless night. Rising at dawn, he went with the villagers to the top of a hill where the elder put down his hat.

   ©Perfection Learning® • No Reproduction Permitted.

After placing his thousand rubles on top, Pakhom began walking, digging holes along the way to mark his land. The going was easy and he thought, "I'll do another three miles and then turn left. The land's so beautiful here, it would be a pity to miss any."

Pakhom hurried throughout the morning, going out of his way to add more land. But at noon when he looked back at the hill where he had begun, it was difficult to see the people. Maybe I have gone too far, he worried, and decided he must begin to make shorter sides. As the afternoon wore on, the heat was exhausting. By now his bare feet were cut and bruised, and his legs weakened. He wanted to rest, but it was out of the question.

Pakhom struggled on, walking faster, then running. He worried that he had been too greedy and his fear made him breathless. On he ran, his shirt soaked and his throat parched. His lungs were working like a blacksmith's bellows, his heart beat like a hammer. He was terrified.

All this strain will be the death of me [said Pakhom to himself]. Although Pakhom feared death, he couldn't stop. They'd call me an idiot, he thought. When he was close enough to hear the Bashkirs cheering, he summoned his last ounce of strength and kept running. As he finally reached the hill, everything suddenly became dark—the sun had set. Pakhom groaned. He wanted to stop, but heard the Bashkirs still cheering him on. He realized that from where he was at the bottom of the hill, the sun had set—but not for those on top. Pakhom took a deep breath and rushed up the hill. Reaching the top, he saw the elder sitting by the hat, laughing his head off. Pakhom's legs gave way, and he fell forward grasping the cap.

"Oh, well done," exclaimed the elder.

"That's a lot of land you've earned yourself!"

Pakhom's worker ran up and tried to lift his master, but Pakhom was dead. The worker picked up Pakhom's spade, dug a grave, and buried him—six feet from head to heel, exactly the amount of land a man needs.

Step 3. Organize your ideas.

Create an outline of the basic events in the story as described in the source. Add new information from your imagination about the characters and the tone of what happened. Below is a sample outline for one possible version of "How Much Land Does a Man Need?" told from the viewpoint of the worker.

Other Organizing Ideas

Outlines are an excellent way to organize information. They work for all types of writing. At a glance, a writer can see which ideas are broader than others. If you create your outline on a computer, adding additional details is simple.

Another way to organize information is with a time line. In a narrative that consists of a series of events, a time line works well. If you are gathering information from several sources, or if the order of events is hard to follow, a time line may be very helpful.

Sample Outline: Just in Case

I. **Pakhom has an opportunity to escape poverty.**
   A. I was hired by Pakhom to go with him on his trip to the land of the Bashkirs.
   B. Pakhom could get all the land he could walk around in one day for just 1,000 rubles.

II. **Pakhom walks for his family.**
   A. Pakhom explained why he is ambitious.
   B. He seemed worried that something bad could happen.
   C. He started strong, but got tired, and died right after he finished.

III. **Pakhom achieved his goal.**
   A. He reminded me of the story of Icarus because he tried to do too much and paid with his life.
   B. I claimed the land he had won.
      1. I sold the land to the Bashkirs.
      2. I gave the money to his widow.
   C. Pakhom died trying to improve his life and the lives of his children.

Step 4. Write the draft.

Using your notes and your outline, write the first draft of your narrative. The following sample draft includes errors that you will correct in later activities.

Sample Draft: Just in Case

"Ivan," Pakhom declared, "I want to hire you to join me on a two-week trip to the land of the Bashkirs and back." I took his statement as an order that he was giving and that he was telling me what to do, rather than a request or suggestion. Pakhom, a small, wirey man who was tenacious as a terrier, knew me because I had often worked for him in his fields. He believed that I was an honest person whom he could trust. "For a fee of 1,000 rubles, the Bashkirs will give him all of the land I walk around in one day. I want you there just in case."

I agreed to go and told him I would. However, as I did I also wondered exactly what he meant when he said "just in case."

We left the next day. As we walked, we talked. "I know some people, especially well-off nobles, don't like me," Pakhom confessed. "They say I am ambitious. I am. I am ambitious for my wife to have a warm coat, for my children to attend school, and for my family never to be hungry. I owe it to my family to do all I can with this amazing opportunity. I will. You watch. I don't really care about owning land so far from home, but I want my family to have a better life. Remember this, just just in case." There was that phrase again. It made me nervous.

The next morning, Pakhom placed his money on the village elder's hat, and marched off to the east. As he started, I felt like a parent, seeing a son going off to war. I was so proud and yet so uneasy that all I could say was simply, "Best wishes, master." Pakhom started strong. However, by mid-day, he was slowing down. My unease turned to fear. As the sun fell lower in the sky, I could see him racing to return in time. To my amazement, he did. Even the village elder was impressed. "Oh well done!" he exclaimed. Then Pakhom died. Now I knew what he meant by "just in case." I cried as I buried him.

As I think back about Pakhom, he reminds me of that young man in Greek mythology named Icarus. He learned to fly to escape a miserable life in Crete, but he got too close to the sun and he died. Like Pakhom, he tried too much. He paid with his life.

However, I had business to take care of. As the elder started off with the 1000 rubles, I stopped him. "The money is yours, but since Pakhom had completed the task on time, the land belongs to his family." The elder was startled, but could not argue.

I knew what Pakhom wanted. As his representative, I immediately sold the land to the Bashkirs. When I returned home, and I had to tell the news to Pakhom's widow. "Your husband died a heroic death. This will not replace him, but it will fulfill his dream." I handed her a thick stack of rubles. Pakhom's family had all the money they would ever need—just in case.

T *Activity 6B Analyzing a Draft*

Answer the following questions about the sample draft.

1. According to the servant, what motivates Pakhom?

_____

2. Identify three transition words or phrases that connect sentences.

_____

3. Give one example of figurative language used in the sample.

_____

Step 5. Revise your narrative.

After you write a draft, read it again carefully. Revise it to eliminate wordiness. In particular, look for words that are say something already said. Consider this sentence. "I took his statement as an order that he was giving and that he was telling me what to do, rather than as a request or suggestion." Shortening it to "I took his statement as an order, not a request" is more direct and just as clear.

T *Activity 6C Eliminating Wordiness*

Rewrite each of these phrases from the sample draft to make it shorter and yet express the same information.

1. "I was an honest person whom he could trust."

_____

_____

2. "I agreed to go and told him I would."

_____

3. "However, as I did I also wondered exactly what he meant when he said 'just in case.'"

_____

_____

Step 6. Edit and proofread your narrative.

After you revise your draft, edit it to be sure you are following the conventions of spelling, punctuation, grammar, and usage.

> **Collaboration on Revision**
>
> Work with a classmate on revising your drafts. Each of you should read the other's draft aloud. As you listen to what you have written, note anything you want to revise. Often, you can hear weaknesses that you do not notice when you read your own work silently to yourself.

> **Technology and Spelling**
>
> On a computer, spell-check can catch many of your errors, but not all of them. The following sentence includes six words that are not spelled correctly as they are used in this sentence:
>
> *Spell-check will not fined words witch are miss used butt spelled rite.*
>
> This sentence should read:
>
> *Spell check will not find words which are misused but spelled right.*

LESSON 7 YOU TRY IT

Now it is your turn to write a narrative. Use the steps outlined in this chapter:

Step 1. Analyze the prompt.

Step 2. Take notes on sources.

Step 3. Organize your ideas.

Step 4. Write the draft.

Step 5. Revise your narrative.

Step 6. Edit and proofread your narrative.

Activity 7A *Writing a Narrative*

Choose one of the following prompts and write a narrative in response to it.

A. Writing a Prequel	B. A School Controversy
A prequel is a story that occurs before another one. Write a two- to four-page narrative about a literary character that occurs before the story in which he or she becomes well-known. For example, write about Dorothy's life before the tornado transported her to Oz or the childhood of the Greek hero Odysseus.	Find multiple news reports about banning a school book or some other controversy in a school. Write a two- to four-page narrative about the event, adding dialogue and description that is consistent with the facts you find.

My writing has . . .	
DEVELOPMENT	❏ a clear experience or event to tell ❏ narrative techniques to develop experiences, events, and characters
ORGANIZATION	❏ a problem, situation, or observation to engage the reader ❏ a clear introduction, body, and conclusion ❏ good transitions to maintain the flow of ideas ❏ events that build on one another to create a coherent whole
EVIDENCE	❏ well-chosen details ❏ well-structured event sequences
LANGUAGE & STYLE	❏ precise words and phrases ❏ telling details ❏ sensory language
GRAMMAR, SPELLING, & PUNCTUATION	❏ standard grammar ❏ correct spelling ❏ proper punctuation

©Perfection Learning® • No Reproduction Permitted.

Chapter 7

Tips for Success

You will demonstrate your skills and communicate your ideas most successfully if you focus on the fundamentals. This chapter focuses on the basic principles of revising essays, taking tests, speaking clearly, and listening effectively.

LESSON 1 TEN TIPS FOR QUICK REVISION

You may not have much time to revise an essay on a test. As a result, you will want to decide quickly what to fix. Here is a list of actions to take.

- ❑ 1. Reread your main idea carefully. It should be stated precisely and clearly.

- ❑ 2. Compare your introduction and your conclusion. They should both address the main idea.

- ❑ 3. Be sure your body paragraphs have enough details, such as relevant evidence, well-chosen facts, precise words, and sensory language.

- ❑ 4. Check for appropriate and varied transitions between paragraphs and between sentences.

- ❑ 5. Read your essay silently, but slowly, word-by-word, as if you were giving a speech. Revise any awkward words or phrases.

- ❑ 6. Look for words you might have omitted or written twice.

- ❑ 7. Check the style and tone of the essay. Usually, you should use a formal style and objective tone.

- ❑ 8. Check that each pronoun refers clearly to a noun and is used correctly.

- ❑ 9. Insert commas where they are necessary. Delete commas where they are not.

- ❑ 10. Correct any misspelled words. If you are writing your essay on a computer, some of these may be highlighted by the word processing program.

©Perfection Learning® • No Reproduction Permitted.

T Activity 1A Applying the Tips

Below is an essay analyzing the writing style of Rudyard Kipling in "Rikki-tikki-tavi." In the blanks on the right, revise each underlined word or phrase. At the end of the change, write the number of the tip that addresses this type of mistake.

Have you ever fought to protect something? In the story "Rikki-tikki-tavi" by Rudyard (1) <u>Kipling a</u> young mongoose overcomes many challenges to save his friends. This story is about a mongoose named Rikki-tikki-tavi who protects a family of humans from deadly snakes. Kipling employs varied sentence structures and figurative language (2) <u>when he writes.</u>

Kipling shows his (3) <u>writing</u> style when he describes Rikki-tikki: "his eyes and the end of his restless nose were pink; he could scratch himself anywhere he pleased with any leg, front or back, that he chose to use; he could fluff up his tail till it looked like a bottle brush . . ." This passage shows the (4) <u>words</u> that the author uses to create a literary style. Because of this, readers can clearly picture the mongoose (5) <u>in in</u> their minds.

Another place (6) <u>the shines</u> through is when Rikki-tikki is in the garden witnessing the distress of two birds. "The nest swayed to and fro, as they sat on the rim and cried." Kipling writes a short, simple sentence here, which is also an element of literary style. (7) <u>He</u> pays attention to the birds. Varied sentence structures make the text much more interesting.

Later in the tale, one of the main antagonists, Nag, has "coiled himself down, coil by coil, around the bulge at the bottom of the water jar, and Rikki-tikki stayed as still as death." The figurative language (8) <u>that is used by the author Kipling</u> further shows the style and adds to the sense of danger and suspense.

Kipling describes (9) <u>anoter</u> character, a bird named Darzee, as "very much like a man in some ways." This use of a comparison with people is another demonstration of Kipling's writing style. (10) <u>Therefore,</u> Kipling develops the traits of (11) <u>Darzee, and</u> brings this character to life.

Kipling's literary writing style is a very important aspect of the story of Rikki-tikki-tavi. In the way Kipling develops describes characters, varies his sentences, and uses figurative language, he creates a wonderful story.

1. _____

2. _____

   _____

3. _____

4. _____

5. _____

6. _____

7. _____

8. _____

   _____

9. _____

10. _____

11. _____

LESSON 2 GENERAL TEST-TAKING TIPS

Each chapter in this book offers tips and strategies that will help you in all writing that you do. The following five tips are particularly useful for writing well on a test.

☐ 1. Before the test, if you feel nervous, prepare yourself to concentrate. Close your eyes or focus on something that is not distracting. Take several slow, deep breaths. Remind yourself to relax.

☐ 2. Begin the test by quickly previewing all the prompts. This will tell what the test is about and how many texts you will write.

☐ 3. Read each prompt carefully. Locate key words or phrases that will help you find the subject of the assignment.

☐ 4. Plan your time for each task. Allow a few minutes at the beginning of each task for prewriting and a few minutes at the end for revising. Use most of the time for writing.

☐ 5. As you begin to respond to each prompt, organize your thoughts about the topic. Use graphic organizers or outlines if they help you get your thoughts down quickly. Then begin writing.

 Activity 2A Summarizing the General Tips

Rewrite each of the five tips listed above as short lines of dialogue. For example, the first tip could be, "Remember to breathe."

1. _____

2. _____

3. _____

4. _____

5. _____

Finish Writing Before You Edit

Plan to save time to revise your writing. However, don't stop writing to revise. Finishing all tasks is more important than revising any single one.

Memory Devices

Connecting the test-taking tips in a story makes them easier to remember. Similarly, which set of words do you think is easier to remember?

- tests year school start students take often to the

- students often take tests to start the school year

The words are the same in both sets. However, since those in the second set are presented in the order of a single sentence, they are easier to remember. If you want to remember a set of key words, combine them into a sentence or short story.

©Perfection Learning® • No Reproduction Permitted.

Activity 2B Writing About a Test

Write a short narrative that includes the five lines of dialogue that you wrote in the previous activity. The narrative does not need to be about taking a test. For example, the line, "Remember to breathe" might be something a basketball coach says to a player learning to shoot free throws or a director says to an actor in a play rehearsal. Use your story to help you remember the five test-taking tips.

_____

_____

_____

_____

_____

_____

_____

_____

_____

_____

_____

_____

_____

_____

_____

_____

_____

_____

_____

_____

_____

_____

©Perfection Learning® • No Reproduction Permitted.

LESSON 3 TIPS FOR SPEAKING AND LISTENING

Like reading, listening is a way to gather information. Like writing, speaking is a way to share what you know and think. The following list of tips will help you speak and listen effectively.

Evaluating Speaking and Listening Skills

To become more familiar with the tips presented on this page, apply them to discussions held by others. Listen to a panel discussion on a television show. Evaluate how well the participants followed the tips.

- ☐ 1. Prepare for a discussion by planning what you want to say. Know the evidence you want to refer to that supports your point.

- ☐ 2. Follow the rules of the discussion. Understand how often you should speak and how long you can speak.

- ☐ 3. Ask specific questions of other individuals in the discussion. Answer questions asked of you.

- ☐ 4. Review key ideas. Reflect on what they mean and practice paraphrasing them.

- ☐ 5. Identify a speaker's claims. Distinguish those that are supported by reasons and evidence and those that are not.

- ☐ 6. Interpret any images, graphics, or music that a speaker uses.

- ☐ 7. When presenting your idea orally, use appropriate eye contact, adequate volume, and clear pronunciation.

- ☐ 8. Use multimedia components, such as graphics, images, music, and sound, in your presentation.

- ☐ 9. Adapt your presentation to the context and the task.

Activity 3A Engaging in Discussion

Participate in a small group discussion about a topic about which you have or can gather much solid information. When your group is done, answer these questions about your discussion.

1. How well did members of the group refer to evidence on the topic?

_____

2. How polite were members of the group toward each other?

_____

3. How well did members of the group ask and respond to specific questions raised in the discussion?

_____

©Perfection Learning® • No Reproduction Permitted.

Activity 3B Interpreting Speeches

Take notes as you listen to a video of a speech or lecture on the Internet that presents an argument. Then answer the following questions about what you heard.

1. What was the speaker's argument? Identify the specific claims made by the speaker.

   _____

   _____

   _____

2. What reasons and evidence did the speaker provide to support his or her claims?

   _____

   _____

   _____

   _____

3. Explain whether you think the reasons and evidence supported the specific claims strongly or not.

   _____

   _____

   _____

Collaboration on Speaking and Listening

Practice your speaking and listening skills with a partner. Discuss a topic of mutual interest for two minutes. Then summarize what the other person has said. Check that each of you has spoken your ideas clearly and has listened accurately.

Activity 3C Practicing a Speech

Have a friend videotape you as you present a one-minute excerpt from a famous speech. Review the videotape together and evaluate your speech on these issues:

1. Did you use appropriate eye contact?

   _____

2. Did you speak loudly enough to be heard easily?

   _____

3. Was your pronunciation clear?

   _____

Notes